WORLD HISTORY

PERSPECTIVES ON THE PAST

Independent Practice Worksheets

The Independent Practice Worksheets were developed by Virginia S. Wilson and James A. Litle, instructors of History/Social Science at the North Carolina School of Science and Mathematics.

This component provides a one-page reinforcement exercise for each section of WORLD HISTORY: Perspectives on the Past. Each worksheet is designed to aid student comprehension of the content of that section. An Answer Key follows the worksheets.

D.C. Heath and Company
Lexington, Massachusetts Toronto, Ontario

Contents for Independent Practice Worksheets

Unit I ***The Beginnings of Civilization***

Chapter 1 Prehistoric Times
Section 1 1
Section 2 2
Section 3 3

Chapter 2 Civilizations and Empires in Southwest Asia
Section 1 4
Section 2 5
Section 3 6

Chapter 3 Ancient Egypt
Section 1 7
Section 2 8
Section 3 9

Chapter 4 Ancient India and China
Section 1 10
Section 2 11
Section 3 12
Section 4 13

Unit II ***The Mediterranean World***

Chapter 5 Ancient Greece
Section 1 14
Section 2 15
Section 3 16
Section 4 17

Chapter 6 The Roman Republic
Section 1 18
Section 2 19
Section 3 20

Chapter 7 The Roman Empire
Section 1 21
Section 2 22
Section 3 23
Section 4 24

Unit III ***The Middle Ages***

Chapter 8 The Byzantine Empire and the Rise of Islam
Section 1 25
Section 2 26
Section 3 27

Chapter 9 The Early Middle Ages
Section 1 28
Section 2 29
Section 3 30
Section 4 31

Chapter 10 The High Middle Ages
Section 1 32
Section 2 33
Section 3 34
Section 4 35
Section 5 36

Chapter 11 The Origin of European Nations
Section 1 37
Section 2 38
Section 3 39
Section 4 40
Section 5 41

Unit IV ***An Age of Empires***

Chapter 12 Golden Ages in China and Japan
Section 1 42
Section 2 43
Section 3 44
Section 4 45
Section 5 46

Chapter 13 Civilizations of India and Southeast Asia
Section 1 47

Published simultaneously in Canada
Printed in the United States of America
International Standard Book Number: 0-669-40541-8
3 4 5 6 7 8 9 0 – MZ – 02 01 00 99 98 97

Section 2 48
Section 3 49

Chapter 14 Africa and the Americas
Section 1 50
Section 2 51
Section 3 52
Section 4 53

Unit V *The Spread of New Ideas*

Chapter 15 The Renaissance and Exploration
Section 1 54
Section 2 55
Section 3 56
Section 4 57
Section 5 58

Chapter 16 The Reformation and the Scientific Revolution
Section 1 59
Section 2 60
Section 3 61
Section 4 62

Chapter 17 The Spanish Empire and Shifts in European Power
Section 1 63
Section 2 64
Section 3 65
Section 4 66
Section 5 67

Unit VI *The Transition to Modern Times*

Chapter 18 England: Tudor Queen and Stuart Kings
Section 1 68
Section 2 69
Section 3 70
Section 4 71

Chapter 19 Europe in the Age of the Absolute Monarchs
Section 1 72
Section 2 73
Section 3 74

Chapter 20 Enlightenment in Europe, Revolution in America
Section 1 75
Section 2 76
Section 3 77
Section 4 78
Section 5 79

Chapter 21 The French Revolution and Napoleon
Section 1 80
Section 2 81
Section 3 82
Section 4 83

Unit VII *The Age of European Dominance*

Chapter 22 The Industrial Revolution
Section 1 84
Section 2 85
Section 3 86
Section 4 87

Chapter 23 Restoration, Romanticism, and Revolution
Section 1 88
Section 2 89
Section 3 90
Section 4 91

Chapter 24 Economic Expansion and Nationalism
Section 1 92
Section 2 93
Section 3 94
Section 4 95

Chapter 25 The Age of Imperialism
Section 1 96
Section 2 97
Section 3 98
Section 4 99
Section 5 100
Section 6 101

Chapter 26 The Turn of the Century
Section 1 102
Section 2 103
Section 3 104
Section 4 105
Section 5 106

Unit VIII *Years of Crisis*

Chapter 27 World War I
Section 1 107
Section 2 108
Section 3 109
Section 4 110

Chapter 28 Russia in Revolution
Section 1 111
Section 2 112
Section 3 113
Section 4 114

Chapter 29 Shifts in World Power
Section 1 115
Section 2 116
Section 3 117
Section 4 118

Chapter 30 The Years between the Wars
Section 1 119
Section 2 120
Section 3 121
Section 4 122
Section 5 123

Chapter 31 World War II
Section 1 124
Section 2 125
Section 3 126
Section 4 127

Unit IX *The Modern World*

Chapter 32 Europe in the Cold War Era
Section 1 128
Section 2 129
Section 3 130
Section 4 131

Chapter 33 Change and Conflict in Asia
Section 1 132
Section 2 133
Section 3 134
Section 4 135
Section 5 136

Chapter 34 Nationalism in Africa and the Middle East
Section 1 137
Section 2 138
Section 3 139
Section 4 140
Section 5 141

Chapter 35 The Americas in the Modern World
Section 1 142
Section 2 143
Section 3 144
Section 4 145

Unit X *Perspectives on the Present*

Chapter 36 The Global Village
Section 1 146
Section 2 147
Section 3 148

Chapter 37 From the Cold War to a New Millennium
Section 1 149
Section 2 150
Section 3 151
Section 4 152

***Answer Key* 153**

Name ____________________
Class ______________
Date ______________

Independent Practice Worksheet 1.1

Scientists search for human origins.
(pages 17–20)

Complete the lists that follow.

1. List three artifacts an archaeologist might use to learn more about prehistoric people.

   a. ____________________ c. ____________________

   b. ____________________

2. List three theories that anthropologists have offered to explain why australopithecines walked upright.

   a. ____________________

   b. ____________________

   c. ____________________

3. List two major discoveries made by Mary and Louis Leakey while they were working in Africa.

   a. ____________________

   b. ____________________

4. List three facts about *Homo habilis*.

   a. ____________________

   b. ____________________

   c. ____________________

5. List the three divisions of the Stone Age.

   a. ____________________

   b. ____________________

   c. ____________________

6. List two major achievements of *Homo erectus*.

   a. ____________________

   b. ____________________

Name ____________________

Class ____________________

Date ____________________

Independent Practice Worksheet 1.2

Modern humans spread across the world.

(pages 21–24)

I. Give two details to support each of the following ideas.

1. Neanderthals were caring people who attached importance to an individual's life and death.

   a. ____________________

   b. ____________________

2. Cro-Magnons had a competitive advantage over Neanderthals.

   a. ____________________

   b. ____________________

3. Cro-Magnons launched a technological revolution.

   a. ____________________

   b. ____________________

4. The sewing needle played a key role in improving human life.

   a. ____________________

   b. ____________________

5. Some nineteenth-century European scholars at first refused to believe that prehistoric humans existed.

   a. ____________________

   b. ____________________

II. Change the underlined parts of these sentences to make true statements.

6. The <u>Neanderthals</u> launched a technological revolution.

7. The first evidence prehistoric *Homo sapiens* existed came from the <u>Rio Grande Valley in Texas</u>.

8. The <u>out-of-Africa</u> theory argues that the Neanderthals gradually evolved into anatomically modern humans.

9. Anatomically modern humans are called <u>*Homo sapiens*</u>, the "doubly wise humans."

10. The majority of prehistoric cave paintings have been found in <u>China and India</u>.

Name ____________________

Class ______________

Date ______________

Independent Practice Worksheet 1.3

Neolithic people began to farm.
(pages 24–27)

Complete the following sentences.

1. Robert Braidwood's excavation took place in ____________, a small village in what is today northeastern Iraq.
2. Braidwood's most important finds were charred seeds from cultivated forms of ____________ and ____________.
3. The Neolithic Age witnessed the birth of ____________ and the beginnings of the first ____________.
4. The ____________ is the region that stretched in a large arc from the Persian Gulf to the Mediterranean Sea. It is thought to be the region where ____________ replaced ____________ and ____________.
5. The last Ice Age reached its peak ____________ years ago.
6. As the world became warmer, frequent droughts left the Fertile Crescent more ____________. The new environment supported grasses such as ____________, ____________, and ____________.
7. An estimated ____________ million people inhabited the earth in 10,000 B.C.
8. Hunter-gatherers may have needed as much as ____________ square miles of land to sustain a band of ____________ people.
9. People in Mesoamerica saved and planted the seeds of the ____________, which they used to carry water.
10. Fossil evidence indicates that people in what is now France domesticated ____________ as early as 30,000 years ago.
11. ____________ were not harnessed to a plow until about 4500 B.C.
12. Wild ____________ was first domesticated in the rich delta of the Yangtze River.
13. Farmers in Mexico and Central America learned how to cultivate ____________, ____________, and ____________. Taken together, these three foods provide all the proteins humans need.
14. ____________ was a thriving village located on a fertile plain in what is now south-central Turkey.
15. ____________ is a smooth, dark volcanic glass used to make ____________, ____________, and ____________.

Name ____________________
Class ____________
Date ____________

Independent Practice Worksheet 2.1

Civilization arose in the Fertile Crescent.
(pages 31–37)

I. The following traits set Sumer apart from earlier societies. Tell why each was important to the growth of Sumer.

1. The Growth of Cities ____________________

2. Specialized Jobs ____________________

3. Writing ____________________

4. Advanced Technology ____________________

5. Complex Institutions ____________________

II. Complete the following lists.

6. List the modern-day nations that were part of the Fertile Crescent in ancient times.

a. ____________ d. ____________

b. ____________ e. ____________

c. ____________

7. List three major problems faced by the Sumer society.

a. ____________

b. ____________

c. ____________

8. List the solutions that the Sumerians found to these problems.

a. ____________

b. ____________

c. ____________

Name ____________________

Class __________

Date __________

Independent Practice Worksheet 2.2

Newcomers contributed to civilization.
(pages 38–43)

I. Complete the following sentences.

1. The major contribution of the Babylonians to the ancient world was ______________.
2. Unlike women in other ancient societies, Babylonian women could ________________, ________________, ________________, and ________________.
3. The two most valuable resources of Phoenicia were ________________________ and ________________________.
4. The Phoenicians decreased the number of symbols in the written language of the time from ____________ to ____________.
5. Three advantages of iron over bronze were ________________________, ________________________, and ________________________.

II. Match each action with the appropriate person.

A. Abraham B. Moses C. Saul D. Solomon E. Isaiah

____ 6. United the Jews in a kingdom known as Israel

____ 7. Warned the Jews of God's punishments

____ 8. Settled with his family in Canaan, later known as Palestine

____ 9. Presented the Ten Commandments to the Jewish people

____ 10. Built a permanent home for the Ark of the Covenant

III. Match each item with the civilization with which it is most closely associated.

A. Babylonian B. Phoenician C. Jewish

____ 11. Excellent sailors

____ 12. Cuneiform writing

____ 13. Monotheism

____ 14. The Ten Commandments

____ 15. A code of laws

____ 16. Stele

____ 17. Prophets

____ 18. Trading colonies on Mediterranean islands

____ 19. A special covenant with God

____ 20. Alphabet

Name ____________________

Class ____________

Date ____________

Independent Practice Worksheet 2.3

Conquerors ruled over larger empires.
(pages 43–49)

I. Complete the following paragraphs by adding facts and details that support each topic sentence.

1. The Assyrian Empire
   The Assyrians had the most disciplined and well-equipped army in the ancient world. ________

2. The Chaldean Empire
   In the sixth century B.C., Babylon was a wonder of the ancient world. ________

3. The Persian Empire
   During the sixth and fifth centuries B.C., Persian kings ruled their empire efficiently and wisely.

II. Rewrite the following false statements to make them true.

4. Most Babylonians, Chaldeans, Assyrians, and Persians were *monotheists.*

5. The *Babylonians* made the city of Babylon a showplace in the sixth century B.C.

6. The Persian empire stretched from the *Hwang He* River to the *Jordan* River to the *Caspian* Sea.

7. The Royal Road of the *Assyrians* ran from Susa, the *Assyrian* capital, to Sardis in *Syria.*

8. *Assurbanipal's* army conquered and burned the city of Jerusalem.

Name ______________________

Class ____________

Date ____________

Independent Practice Worksheet 3.1

Egypt arose in Africa's Nile Valley.
(pages 53–57)

I. Rewrite the following false statements to make them true.

1. *Lower* Egypt stretched from the First Cataract to where the Nile River branches; *Upper* Egypt began approximately 100 miles south of the mouth of the Nile River on the Mediterranean Sea.

2. The Nile River flooded every *October.*

3. Egyptian villages were built along the *desert borders.*

4. In time, Egyptian villages united into *city-states.*

5. The capital of united Egypt was located at *Thebes.*

II. Listed below are a number of causes. For each cause, state the most significant effect or effects.

6. *Cause:* The Nile flows north.

   Effect: ____

   ____

7. *Cause:* Every year the Nile flooded its banks.

   Effect: ____

   ____

8. *Cause:* The Nile left behind a deposit of fertile black soil.

   Effect: ____

   ____

9. *Cause:* Sometimes the Nile's floodwaters were less than expected.

   Effect: ____

   ____

10. *Cause:* Vast desert areas surrounded the Nile valley.

    Effect: ____

    ____

Name ____________________

Class ____________

Date ____________

Independent Practice Worksheet 3.2

Egypt's pharaohs ruled as gods.
(pages 58–63)

Give two details to support each of the following main ideas.

1. Egyptian pharaohs were more than political leaders.

   a. ____________________

   b. ____________________

2. Peasants, not slaves, built the Great Pyramid at Giza.

   a. ____________________

   b. ____________________

3. Trade grew and farming revived under the pharaohs of the Middle Kingdom.

   a. ____________________

   b. ____________________

4. The Egyptians learned many things from the Hyksos.

   a. ____________________

   b. ____________________

5. Thutmose III was a warlike ruler.

   a. ____________________

   b. ____________________

6. The New Kingdom was an age of great buildings.

   a. ____________________

   b. ____________________

Name ______________________
Class __________
Date __________

Independent Practice Worksheet 3.3

Egypt's way of life endured 3,000 years.
(pages 63–69)

Complete the lists that follow.

1. List five positions that an Egyptian noble might hold in the pharaoh's service.

   a. ______________________ d. ______________________

   b. ______________________ e. ______________________

   c. ______________________

2. List six rights of Egyptian women that were unusual in ancient times.

   a. ______________________ d. ______________________

   b. ______________________ e. ______________________

   c. ______________________ f. ______________________

3. List four types of work that were open to those who could read and write.

   a. ______________________ c. ______________________

   b. ______________________ d. ______________________

4. List four jobs done by peasants.

   a. ______________________ c. ______________________

   b. ______________________ d. ______________________

5. List five major duties of Egyptian house slaves.

   a. ______________________ d. ______________________

   b. ______________________ e. ______________________

   c. ______________________

6. List two facts that show the power and prestige of Egyptian priests.

   a. ______________________ b. ______________________

7. List five fields in which Egyptians had a reputation for knowledge.

   a. ______________________ d. ______________________

   b. ______________________ e. ______________________

   c. ______________________

Name ____________________

Class ______________

Date ______________

Independent Practice Worksheet 4.1

A new culture arose in northern India.
(pages 73–78)

Identify a possible cause or reason for each of the following effects.

1. *Effect:* Indian farmers sometimes suffer from too much or too little rain.

   Cause: ____________________

2. *Effect:* Around 1750 B.C., Indus valley cities became poorer.

   Cause: ____________________

3. *Effect:* Between 1500 and 500 B.C., a new society took shape in northern India.

   Cause: ____________________

4. *Effect:* Hindu practices include ideas of both the Indus valley dwellers and the Aryans.

   Cause: ____________________

5. *Effect:* Hindus considered high castes to be purer than low castes.

   Cause: ____________________

Name ______________________

Class ____________

Date ____________

Independent Practice Worksheet 4.2

Buddhism spread under Mauryan rulers.
(pages 79–82)

I. Who am I? Match the correct person(s) with the following statements by placing the correct letter(s) in the blank.

A. Gautama   B. Ashoka   C. Chandragupta

_____ 1. I believed that all living things should be treated with loving kindness.

_____ 2. I taught that the way to end all pain was to end all desires.

_____ 3. I believed in rule by force and fear.

_____ 4. I suffered remorse for the slaying of 100,000 captives.

_____ 5. I taught that anyone, rich or poor, could escape the cycle of death and rebirth.

_____ 6. I believed that if a person followed the Eightfold Path, he or she would attain nirvana.

_____ 7. I believed that no one was to be trusted.

_____ 8. I united northern India.

_____ 9. I believed that life was an endless sorrow.

_____ 10. I employed "officials of righteousness."

_____ 11. As a ruler, I accepted the religion of Buddhism.

_____ 12. I believed in nonviolence.

_____ 13. I sent Buddhist missionaries to neighboring lands.

_____ 14. I believed in government spies.

_____ 15. I used stone pillars to announce my policies.

II. Complete the following sentences.

16. Gautama chose to leave his wife and son because he thought that ____________________.

17. People elect to follow the Eightfold Path in order to attain ______________________________.

18. Buddhism was attractive to the people of India because it ______________________________ and ______________________________.

19. The Second Noble Truth is that pain is caused by ______________________________.

20. Buddhism spread far beyond India partly because of the encouragement of ____________________.

Name ______________
Class ______
Date ______

Independent Practice Worksheet 4.3

Imperial government united China.
(pages 82–88)

For each of the following topics on ancient China, supply at least two facts from your textbook.

1. *Topic:* Family
   Facts:

   a. ______________________________

   b. ______________________________

2. *Topic:* Government
   Facts:

   a. ______________________________

   b. ______________________________

3. *Topic:* Yellow River
   Facts:

   a. ______________________________

   b. ______________________________

4. *Topic:* Confucius
   Facts:

   a. ______________________________

   b. ______________________________

5. *Topic:* Lao Tzu
   Facts:

   a. ______________________________

   b. ______________________________

6. *Topic:* The Legalists
   Facts:

   a. ______________________________

   b. ______________________________

Name ______________________

Class ____________

Date ____________

Independent Practice Worksheet 4.4

Ch'in and Han emperors strengthened China.
(pages 89–93)

I. Identify when each of the following events occurred by placing the correct letter from the timeline in the blank.

A		B		C		D
300 B.C.	250		200		150	100 B.C.

____ 1. The ruler of China became known as the emperor.

____ 2. Wu-ti's rule began.

____ 3. Ch'in armies destroyed the Chou forces.

____ 4. Confucianism was proclaimed as the official set of beliefs for the Chinese government.

____ 5. All noble families had to live in the capital.

____ 6. China's land area doubled from what it had been under the Chou dynasty.

____ 7. The silk trade linked China and the rest of the civilized world.

____ 8. The Han dynasty began.

____ 9. A national university was founded.

____ 10. The Great Wall was constructed.

II. Complete the following sentences.

11. The First Emperor concentrated on the tasks of destroying ______________________ and ______________________.

12. The First Emperor weakened the warlords by ______________________________

13. The years of Han rule were a time of ____________, ____________, and ____________.

14. The curriculum at the national university included ____________ and ____________.

15. Buddhism entered China by way of traders from the ______________________ and ______________________.

Name ______________________

Class ____________

Date ____________

Independent Practice Worksheet 5.1

Greek culture grew up around the Aegean Sea.
(pages 103–108)

I. Tell how each of the following geographic features shaped Greek civilization.

1. The sea

____

____

____

2. The land

____

____

____

II. Compare and contrast the Minoan, Mycenaean, and Dorian civilizations by completing the following chart.

	Minoan civilization	Mycenaean civilization	Dorian civilization
3. Location	(a)	(b)	(c)
4. Date civilization at height	(a)	(b)	(c)
5. Major trade partners	(a)	(b)	(c)
6. Reason for decline	(a)	(b)	X
7. Significant events, contributions	(a)	(b)	(c)

Name ______________________
Class ____________
Date ____________

Independent Practice Worksheet 5.2

Greek city-states competed for power.
(pages 108–114)

Identify the most probable cause of each effect.

1. Ordinary citizens could now afford to serve in the army of Greece.

   Cause: ____

   ____

2. Tyrants built great forts, harbors, and temples.

   Cause: ____

   ____

3. The Spartans lived in fear of a helot uprising.

   Cause: ____

   ____

4. Solon prevented a civil war.

   Cause: ____

   ____

5. Athens had a nearly complete democracy.

   Cause: ____

   ____

6. Athens and Sparta were spurred to their greatest glory.

   Cause: ____

   ____

7. The Greeks defeated the Persians at Salamis.

   Cause: ____

   ____

8. Athens became the leader of the Delian League.

   Cause: ____

   ____

Name ____________________

Class ____________

Date ____________

Independent Practice Worksheet 5.3

Athens led Greece in its golden age.
(pages 115–122)

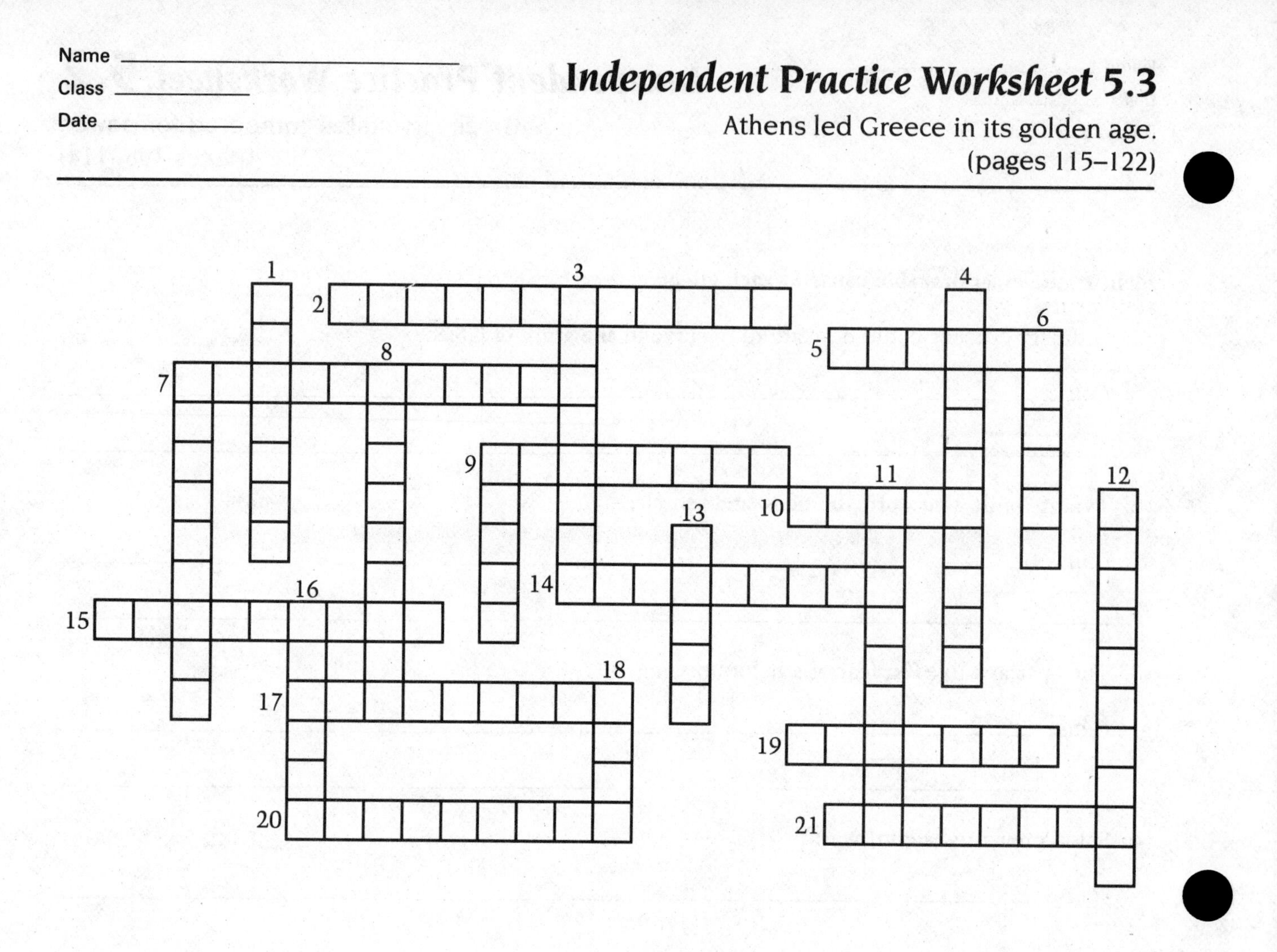

ACROSS

2. The first writer of comedies
5. The strongest land power in Greece
7. One who loves wisdom
9. One of Greece's greatest philosophers
10. A standard of classical art
14. Three logically related statements
15. Two great ramparts that protected the roadway from Athens to the sea
17. Thucydides, for example
19. A drama in which a hero's strength lead to his or her downfall
20. Developed the syllogism
21. One of Sparta's wealthiest allies

DOWN

1. Created the statue of Athena
3. The man who dominated Athens for 32 years
4. A standard of classical art
6. The strongest sea power in Greece
7. A Greek temple considered one of world's noblest works of architecture
8. Wrote *Oedipus*
9. One who did the hard work in Athens
11. The government of Athens
12. Wrote the history of the Peloponnesian War
13. Wrote *The Republic*
16. Her statue stood within the Parthenon
18. The Greek word for victory

Name ______________________

Class ____________

Date ____________

Independent Practice Worksheet 5.4

Alexander's conquests spread Greek culture.
(pages 122–127)

I. In the space provided, write the name of the person who would have made each of the following statements.

______________________ 1. I used geometry to compute the earth's circumference at about 25,000 miles.

______________________ 2. I assassinated Philip II.

______________________ 3. I lost the Persian empire when Alexander defeated me at the battle of Gaugamela.

______________________ 4. I tried to warn the Athenians that Philip was ruthless and had to be stopped.

______________________ 5. Philip divorced me and married the daughter of a high-ranking Macedonian nobleman.

______________________ 6. I called upon Philip to unite the Greeks and then take the offensive against Persia.

______________________ 7. I soundly defeated the Athenians and Thebans at the battle of Chaeronea.

______________________ 8. I calculated the value of pi (π) and discovered that levers could be used to lift heavy objects.

______________________ 9. I opened a school of geometry in Alexandria.

______________________ 10. I conquered the Persian empire.

II. Fill in the blanks with the word or words that correctly complete each statement.

11. A vibrant new culture called ______________________ emerged from the blend of Greek and eastern customs.

12. The Macedonian army featured dense ______________________, 16 men across and 16 deep.

13. Alexander led an elite cavalry unit known as the ______________________.

14. Alexandria's greatest attractions were its famous ______________________ and ______________________.

15. The ______________________ was a famous Hellenistic statue discovered in 1863.

Name ______________________

Class ____________

Date ____________

Independent Practice Worksheet 6.1

The Romans built a great city.
(pages 131–134)

I. Show the influence of the Greeks and Etruscans on the Latin settlers of the Italian peninsula by completing the following chart.

	Greeks	Etruscans
1. Place of origin	(a)	(b)
2. Arrival in Italy	(a)	(b)
3. Contributions to Roman religion	(a)	(b)
4. Other Contributions	(a)	(b)

II. List two facts about each of the following concepts or ideas.

5. *Concept:* Roman republic

   a. ______________________________

   b. ______________________________

6. *Concept:* Roman family

   a. ______________________________

   b. ______________________________

7. *Concept:* Social class

   a. ______________________________

   b. ______________________________

8. *Concept:* Roman army

   a. ______________________________

   b. ______________________________

Name ____________________

Class ____________

Date ____________

Independent Practice Worksheet 6.2

The Roman republic spread its power.
(pages 135–140)

List at least one effect for each of the following causes.

1. Between 494 and 287 B.C., disgruntled plebeians sometimes refused to fight in the Roman army.
   Effect:
   ____

2. Rome was sacked by the Gauls in 390 B.C.
   Effect:
   ____

3. Pyrrhus attacked Rome in 282 B.C.
   Effect:
   ____

4. A Carthaginian warship washed ashore on the Italian peninsula.
   Effect:
   ____

5. Rome and Carthage fought the First Punic War.
   Effect:
   ____

6. In 218 B.C., Hannibal invaded Italy.
   Effect:
   ____

7. In 202 B.C., Scipio attacked Carthage.
   Effect:
   ____

8. The people of Corinth rebelled against Roman rule.
   Effect:
   ____

Name ______________________

Class ____________

Date ____________

Independent Practice Worksheet 6.3

Republican government collapsed in Rome.
(pages 141–147)

I. Complete the following sentences.

1. The large estates known as latifundia developed because small farmers were forced to ______________________.
2. Many landless workers moved to ______________________.
3. Tribunes spoke on behalf of the ____________.
4. The provinces of Rome in 60 B.C. were ______________________, ______________________, ______________________, ______________________, ______________________, and ______________________.
5. Two changes initiated by Caesar as the absolute ruler of Rome were ______________________ and ______________________.

II. Who am I? Identify the speaker of each statement by placing the correct letter in the blank.

A. Cicero	D. Marius	G. Octavian
B. Julius Caesar	E. Brutus	H. Sulla
C. Mark Anthony	F. Pompey	I. Spartacus

____ 6. I heard Caesar's last words, "Et tu, Brute!"

____ 7. My reign marked the beginning of the longest period of peace and prosperity known to Rome.

____ 8. In 105 B.C., my army saved Rome from an invasion by Germanic tribes.

____ 9. My troops were defeated at Pharsalus in 48 B.C.

____ 10. I was a champion of the senate and a rival of Marius.

____ 11. I was the senate's greatest orator, and I was killed by the Second Triumvirate.

____ 12. I conquered Gaul.

____ 13. I divorced Octavian's sister to marry Cleopatra.

____ 14. I raised an army of 70,000 who were slaves eager to fight for their freedom.

Name ____________________

Class __________

Date __________

Independent Practice Worksheet 7.1

Augustus's rule began the Pax Romana.
(pages 151–154)

Complete the following lists.

1. List six accomplishments of the Romans during the Pax Romana.

   a. ____________________

   b. ____________________

   c. ____________________

   d. ____________________

   e. ____________________

   f. ____________________

2. List three ways in which Augustus made trade within the empire easier.

   a. ____________________

   b. ____________________

   c. ____________________

3. List three responsibilities of Rome's civil servants.

   a. ____________________

   b. ____________________

   c. ____________________

4. List two problems that the government faced during the Pax Romana.

   a. ____________________

   b. ____________________

5. List two events that weakened the empire during the Pax Romana.

   a. ____________________

   b. ____________________

Name ____________________

Class __________

Date __________

Independent Practice Worksheet 7.2

Romans extended Greek culture.
(pages 155–160)

I. Who am I? Identify the speaker of each statement by placing the correct letter in the blank. Two letters will be used more than once.

A. Epicurus
B. Tacitus
C. Livy
D. Virgil
E. Zeno
F. Marcus Aurelius
G. Juvenal
H. Augustus Caesar

____ 1. I wrote the history of Rome for Augustus.

____ 2. I wrote a journal that became a book called the *Meditations.*

____ 3. I wrote an epic poem, the *Aeneid.*

____ 4. I saved the *Aeneid* from destruction.

____ 5. I taught that the universe was controlled by a superhuman power.

____ 6. I was an emperor and a noted Stoic.

____ 7. I directed my scorn at the Roman government.

____ 8. I taught that death was the end of all existence.

____ 9. I wrote about the morals of Rome's private citizens.

____ 10. I wrote patriotic works that showed the old heroes as men of honor and moral strength.

II. Complete the following sentences.

11. The Romans admired the Greek accomplishments in the fields of ____________, ____________, ____________ and ____________.

12. The blending of the Greek and Roman cultures is sometimes referred to as ____________.

13. Greek architecture glorified Greek ____________, while the Roman architecture glorified Roman ____________.

14. The greatest achievement of Roman architecture was the ____________.

Name ________________________
Class ____________
Date ____________

Independent Practice Worksheet 7.3

Christianity spread through the empire.
(pages 160–164)

I. Identify the correct date or dates when the following events took place.

1. Paul took the new Christian religion to the Mediterranean world. ________________________
2. Rome created the province of Judaea. ________________________
3. The beginning of the Zealot revolution that resulted in the burning of the Jewish temple in Jerusalem.

   ____
4. Judas Maccabee recaptured the Jewish temple in Jerusalem. ________________________
5. Approximately 10 percent of the Roman empire had converted to Christianity.

   ____
6. Rome conquered Syria and Palestine. ________________________
7. The Jews won their independence. ________________________
8. Jesus was hailed in Jerusalem as the Messiah and was crucified. ________________________
9. The Jews rebelled soon after Hadrian rebuilt the Jewish temple as a shrine to Jupiter.

   ____
10. Nero ordered the persecution of Christians. ________________________

II. Use your answers to Part I to complete the following activities.

11. Place the events listed above in chronological order.

    ____
12. How many years passed between Rome's conquest of Palestine and Nero's order to persecute Christians?

    ____

Name ____________________
Class ____________
Date ____________

Independent Practice Worksheet 7.4

Rome's empire declined and fell.
(pages 164–169)

I. Following the death of Marcus Aurelius, the Roman empire entered a period of decline because of economic, political, and military problems. List these problems under the appropriate category.

1. Economic problems

   a. ____________________

   b. ____________________

   c. ____________________

   d. ____________________

   e. ____________________

2. Military problems

   a. ____________________

   b. ____________________

   c. ____________________

   d. ____________________

3. Political problems

   a. ____________________

   b. ____________________

   c. ____________________

II. Trade the decline of the western Roman empire by matching each event with the correct date.

____ 4. 311 A. Constantine moved the capital from Rome to Byzantium.

____ 5. 330 B. The Vandals sacked Rome.

____ 6. 376 C. Pope Leo I stopped Attila the Hun's advance on Rome.

____ 7. 406 D. The beginning of a century of destruction by semibarbaric people.

____ 8. 410 E. The Vandals crossed the frozen Rhine River.

____ 9. 452 F. Upon Diocletian's retirement, four rivals competed for power.

____ 10. 455 G. The Visigoths sacked Rome.

Name ______________________
Class ___________
Date __________

Independent Practice Worksheet 8.1

Constantinople ruled an eastern empire.
(pages 179–185)

I. Using the numbers 1–5, place the following statements in chronological order.

____ A. The Byzantines won control over a ruined Rome.

____ B. A plague swept through the empire.

____ C. The Ostrogoths drove the Byzantines from Rome.

____ D. A riot over a chariot race broke out in Constantinople.

____ E. Belisarius conquered Carthage.

II. Complete the following sentences.

6. The Muslims built the Dome of the Rock in the city of ____________.

7. Constantinople was founded in 330 on the site of a seaport known as ____________.

8. The Dardanelles separate the ____________ Sea and the Sea of ____________.

9. The eastern Roman empire included ____________, ____________, ____________, ____________, and ____________.

10. The three important projects undertaken by the Emperor Justinian were ______________________, ______________________, and ______________________.

11. Western Europeans would turn to the Justinian code for answers to questions about ____________, ____________, ____________, and ______________________.

12. Citizenship in Constantinople was based on a person's ______________________ and ______________________.

13. Constantinople was protected by ____________, ____________, and ____________.

14. After 565, the Byzantine empire was racked by ______________________, ______________________, and ______________________.

15. The eastern empire included the areas of Asia Minor, ______________________, ______________________, and ______________________.

Name ______________________
Class ____________
Date ____________

Independent Practice Worksheet 8.2

A new faith spread from Arabia.
(pages 186–193)

I. Explain the significance of the following years to the growth of Islam.

1. 570 ______________________________

2. 613 ______________________________

3. 622 ______________________________

4. 630 ______________________________

5. 732 ______________________________

II. Complete the following lists.

6. List the Five Pillars of Islam.

a. ____________ d. ____________

b. ____________ e. ____________

c. ____________

7. List eight areas that the Muslim Arabs controlled by 732.

a. ____________ e. ____________

b. ____________ f. ____________

c. ____________ g. ____________

d. ____________ h. ____________

8. List the two branches into which Islam split.

a. ____________ b. ____________

Name ____________________

Class __________

Date __________

Independent Practice Worksheet 8.3

The empires influence Slavs and Turks.

(pages 194–197)

I. The Islamic and Byzantine empires declined because of internal divisions and external attacks. In the appropriate category, list the details for these causes.

The Byzantine Empire

1. Internal Divisions (See Section 1.)

   a. ____________________

   b. ____________________

2. External attacks

   a. ____________________

   b. ____________________

   c. ____________________

The Islamic Empire

3. Internal divisions

   The breaking away of

   a. __________ in 756

   b. __________ in 788

   c. __________ in 800

   d. __________ in 809

   e. __________ in 868

4. External attacks

   a. ____________________

   b. ____________________

II. Rewrite the following false statements to make them true.

5. Early Russian civilization centered on the city of *Moscow.*

6. In 1054, the Christian Church split into the *Russian* Church and the *Caliphate* Church.

7. The threat to the Byzantine empire in the 1300's came from the *Chinese.*

8. In 1453, the city of *Baghdad* fell to the *Slavs.*

Name ____________________

Class ____________

Date ____________

Independent Practice Worksheet 9.1

New ways of life developed in Europe.
(pages 200–205)

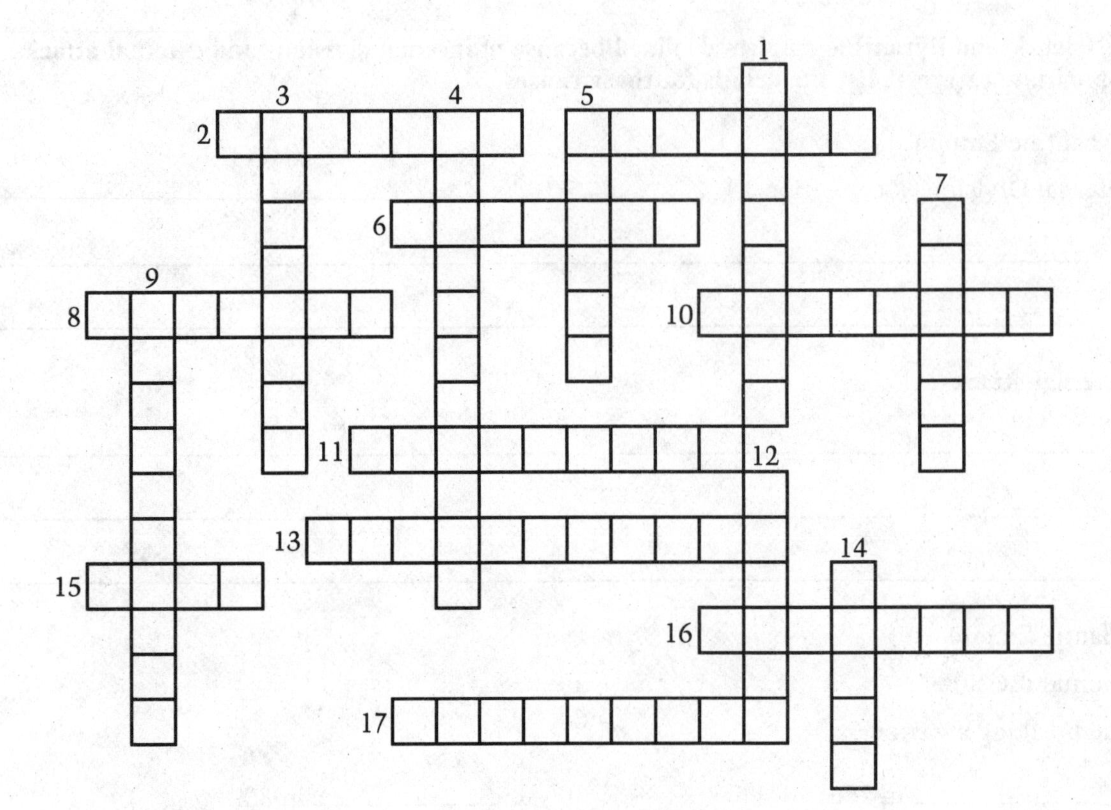

ACROSS

2. Converted the Irish to Christianity
5. A community of nuns
6. The person who increased the pope's power
8. The name given to languages that evolved from Latin
10. The ability to read and write
11. A community of monks
13. Adapted Benedict's rules for women
15. Head of the Catholic Church
16. Invaded Rome in 568
17. The group that held Spain

DOWN

1. The monk who set the pattern for monastic living
3. A branch of Christianity followed by many Germanic Groups
4. A spiritual kingdom fanning out from Rome
5. A Frankish king who became a Christian
7. The group that controlled Gaul
9. The group that ruled Italy
12. A Germanic tribe that attacked Britannia
14. A monastic leader

Name ______________________

Class ____________

Date ____________

Independent Practice Worksheet 9.2

Charlemagne revived the idea of empire.
(pages 206–211)

Complete the following sentences.

1. By the time of Clovis's death, his family ruled most of what is now ______________________.

2. A weakness of the Merovingian kings was their decision to divide the kingdom ____.

3. By 700, the most powerful person in the Frankish kingdom was the ______________________.

4. Officially the major domo was in charge of the ________________ and ________________.

5. Charles Martel was king in all but ______________________.

6. Pepin needed the Church to give his rule ______________________, and the pope needed Pepin for protection against the ______________________.

7. The invention of the ______________________ allowed heavily armed knights to fight on horseback.

8. By 800, Charlemagne's kingdom included ____________, ____________, ____________ and ____________.

9. Under Charlemagne, the Frankish kingdom was divided into __________ ruled by __________.

10. The duties of a count were to ______________________ and ______________________.

11. The ______________________ were sent out to check on the activities of counts.

12. Charlemagne visited every part of his kingdom in order to ____________, ____________, ____________, and ____________.

13. Charlemagne ordered ____________ and ____________ to establish schools to train Church leaders.

14. The Treaty of Verdun divided the kingdom of Charlemagne into the territories of ____________, ____________, and ____________.

15. The lands of Charlemagne's grandson ____________ became the battleground for French and German kings.

Name ______________________

Class ____________

Date ____________

Independent Practice Worksheet 9.3

Vikings terrorized Europe.
(pages 211–214)

Complete the following sentences.

1. Between A.D. 800 and 1000, the Vikings raided from ______________________ to ______________________.

2. The invaders of Lindisfarne Island used ______________________ and ______________________.

3. The Vikings were also known as ______________________ and ______________________.

4. Scandinavia, the land of the Vikings, is made up of the modern-day nations of ______________________, ______________________, and ______________________.

5. Much of the Vikings' advantage in warfare was due to the advanced design of their ____________.

6. By 900, Scandinavian families had settled the island of ____________, and by the end of the century, the island of ______________________.

7. The Viking who led an expedition to the Americas before Columbus was ______________________.

8. Viking warriors were later followed by Viking ______________________, ______________________, and ______________________.

9. Viking attacks gradually ended because of ______________________, ______________________, and ______________________.

10. By the year 1000 the Vikings could ______________________ because of warmer temperatures.

Name ____________________
Class __________
Date __________

Independent Practice Worksheet 9.4

Feudalism became the basis for government.
(pages 214–219)

Medieval writers said that there were three groups of people: those who fought, those who prayed, and those who worked. Describe the rights and responsibilities of each group on a medieval manor.

1. a. Who fought? ____________________

   b. What were their rights?

   ____

   ____

   c. What were their responsibilities?

   ____

   ____

2. a. Who prayed? ____________________

   b. What were their rights?

   ____

   ____

   c. What were their responsibilities?

   ____

   ____

3. a. Who worked? ____________________

   b. What were their rights?

   ____

   ____

   c. What were their responsibilities?

   ____

   ____

Name ____________________

Class ______________

Date ______________

Independent Practice *Worksheet* 10.1

Farming improved and trade revived.
(pages 223–227)

For each development listed below, identify a significant effect.

1. A heavier plow came into use.
   Effect:
   ____
2. A collar that fit across the horse's chest was invented.
   Effect:
   ____
3. Farmers in much of Europe began using the three-field system.
   Effect:
   ____
4. More food became available in Europe.
   Effect:
   ____
5. The population of Europe increased.
   Effect:
   ____
6. Jews were barred from owning land or participating in many businesses.
   Effect:
   ____
7. Serfs were free if they were not caught for a year and a day.
   Effect:
   ____
8. Lords demanded payment from the nearby towns.
   Effect:
   ____

Name ______________________

Class ___________

Date ___________

Independent Practice Worksheet 10.2

Religious leaders wielded great power.
(pages 228–231)

Describe how each of the following furthered Church reform during the Middle Ages.

1. A new monastery founded at Cluny in 910

   a. ______________________________________

   ____

   b. ______________________________________

   ____

2. Church decree of 1059

   ____

   ____

3. Gregory VII

   a. ______________________________________

   ____

   b. ______________________________________

   ____

4. Concordat of Worms

   a. ______________________________________

   ____

   b. ______________________________________

   ____

5. Friars

   a. ______________________________________

   ____

   b. ______________________________________

   ____

Name ____________________
Class ____________
Date ____________

Independent Practice Worksheet 10.3

Royal governments grew stronger.
(pages 233–236)

I. Complete the following sentences.

1. After the conquest, William granted lands to ____________ and ____________.
2. Henry II's greatest achievement was the strengthening of the ____________.
3. The purpose of a jury under Henry II was to ________________________.
4. The rulings made by England's royal judges eventually became known as ________________________.
5. The center of Hugh Capet's territory was the city of ____________.
6. Otto I was able to dominate the churches of Germany by ________________________.
7. The German-Italian empire established by Otto I was known initially as the ________________________ and then later as the ________________________.

II. What event took place in each of the years listed below? To what country was that event important? For what reasons?

8. 987

   Event: ________________________

   Country: ________________________

   Significance: ________________________

9. 1066

   Event: ________________________

   Country: ________________________

   Significance: ________________________

10. 1176

    Event: ________________________

    Country: ________________________

    Significance: ________________________

Name ______________________
Class ____________
Date ____________

Independent Practice Worksheet 10.4

Learning revived and spread.
(pages 237–240)

I. Complete the following sentences.

1. A group of ______________________ was the core of a medieval university.
2. Because writing materials were scarce at medieval universities, most exams were taken ______________________.
3. Most students spent ______ to ______ years at a university to attain a bachelor's degree.
4. A master's degree usually required an additional __________ to __________ years of study.
5. Scholars in all parts of Europe spoke the ______________________ language.
6. Four areas of knowledge that medieval universities emphasized were ______________________, ______________________, ______________________, and ______________________.
7. The *Summa Theologiae* attempted to link ______________________ and ______________________.
8. Typical subjects of heroic poems were ______________________, ______________________, ______________________, and ______________________.
9. The code of chivalry demanded that a knight fight in defense of his ______________________, ______________________, and ______________________.
10. Women had their greatest power during ______________________.

II. Rewrite the following false statements to make them true.

11. *Roland* believed that the most basic religious truths could be proved by logical arguments.
12. Most students at universities were from the *aristocracy.*
13. From the *German* libraries and the city of *Rome,* Europeans brought home translations of Greek and Latin writings.
14. Young noble boys became *squires* first, then *knights,* and finally *pages.*
15. In the high Middle Ages, women had *many* opportunities for careers outside the home and the convent.

Name ____________________
Class ____________
Date ____________

Independent Practice Worksheet 10.5

Crusaders marched against Islam.
(pages 241–245)

Identify the event associated with each date and state the significance of the event.

DATE	EVENT	SIGNIFICANCE
1. 1095		
2. 1099		
3. 1187		
4. 1192		
5. 1202		
6. 1229		

Name ______________________

Class ___________

Date ___________

Independent Practice Worksheet 11.1

England and France developed as nations.
(pages 249–254)

I. Which country does each statement describe? Write the correct letter in the blank.

A. England B. France C. Both England and France

____ 1. In this nation "no free man shall be arrested or imprisoned . . . except by the legal judgment of his peers."

____ 2. People in this nation accepted the idea of a limited monarchy.

____ 3. This nation had a supreme court called the Parlement.

____ 4. From 1066 to 1204, this nation controlled Normandy.

____ 5. Over the years, the townspeople in this nation won a larger share of political power.

____ 6. The king of this nation affixed his seal to the Magna Carta.

____ 7. The king of this nation called for an Estates General, or meeting of all three estates.

____ 8. The king of this nation called together barons and townspeople for a parliament.

____ 9. The central government of this nation was strengthened during the reign of Philip Augustus' grandson.

____ 10. Bailiffs were sent out to every district in this kingdom.

____ 11. In 1302, the king of this nation became involved in a quarrel with the pope.

____ 12. The national assembly of this nation increased royal power at the expense of the nobility.

____ 13. Between 1300 and 1500, this country became a nation-state.

____ 14. In this country, taxes were "levied only by the common consent of the kingdom."

____ 15. Royal courts strengthened the monarchy in this country and weakened the feudal ties.

II. Write a paragraph summarizing similarities and differences in the political growth of England and France. Use characteristics that you identified in the previous exercise.

Name ____________________

Class ______________

Date ______________

Independent Practice Worksheet 11.2

The Church faced a crisis in the 1300's.
(pages 254–256)

Identify an effect of each of the developments that follow.

1. Philip IV taxed the Church of France.

____

2. Pope Boniface VIII tried to force rulers to recognize the supremacy of the Church over the state.

____

3. Political violence in Rome threatened the life of Pope Clement V.

____

4. France became the home of the popes.

____

5. Pope Urban VI had a zeal for reform and an overbearing personality.

____

6. In 1378, Europe had two popes.

____

7. In the 1300's, the old sources of authority collapsed in Europe.

____

8. An English archbishop branded John Wycliffe a heretic.

____

9. John Huss was a spokesperson for Czech national feeling as well as for religious reform.

____

10. The Council of Constance chose Martin V as pope.

____

Name ______________________
Class __________
Date __________

Independent Practice Worksheet 11.3

The 1300's brought plague and war.
(pages 257–261)

Identify the following events, people, or inventions by answering the following questions: Who (or what) was it? What did it do? When? Where? Why was it important?

1. Black Death

   a. What? ______________________

   b. Did what? ______________________

   c. When? ______________ d. Where? ______________

   e. Why? ______________________

2. The Peasant Revolt

   a. What? ______________________

   b. Did what? ______________________

   c. When? ______________ d. Where? ______________

   e. Why? ______________________

3. Hundred Years' War

   a. What? ______________________

   b. Did what? ______________________

   c. When? ______________ d. Where? ______________

   e. Why? ______________________

4. Joan of Arc

   a. Who? ______________________

   b. Did what? ______________________

   c. When? ______________ d. Where? ______________

   e. Why? ______________________

Name ____________________

Class ____________

Date ____________

Independent Practice Worksheet 11.4

New monarchs ruled in western Europe.
(pages 261–264)

I. Identify the country with which each of the following events is associated.

A. England   B. France   C. Spain

____ 1. The duchy of Burgundy became part of this kingdom.

____ 2. Christopher Columbus sailed west across the Atlantic.

____ 3. Henry VII became king.

____ 4. The Court of Star Chamber was used to destroy over-mighty subjects.

____ 5. Charles VII drove out the English.

____ 6. The Wars of the Roses began.

____ 7. Rulers revived the Inquisition in the late 1400's, and many people were executed as heretics.

____ 8. Isabella of Castile and Ferdinand of Aragon were married.

____ 9. The gabelle and the taille were the main sources of royal money.

____ 10. King Richard III was killed in the Battle of Bosworth Field.

____ 11. Granada fell to a Christian army.

____ 12. Navarre south of the Pyrenees was seized by Ferdinand of Aragon.

____ 13. Unlike other new monarchs, the king kept no standing army.

____ 14. Louis XI was known as the Spider King for his plots.

____ 15. All Jews were expelled.

II. For each date, identify the events associated with the rise of the middle class.

16. 1000–1100 ____

17. 1100's ____

18. 1295 ____

19. 1302 ____

20. 1400's ____

Name ____________________
Class __________
Date __________

Independent Practice Worksheet 11.5

A new empire arose in Russia.
(pages 265–267)

I. Complete the following sentences.

1. The northern part of Russia is covered by an immense ____________________, and the southern part by a ____________________.

2. Most rivers of European Russia flow into the ______________, ______________, ______________, or ______________.

3. Control of the ____________________, ____________________, and ____________________ rivers meant control of Russia.

4. The princes of Moscow used ____________________, ____________________, ____________________ and ____________________ to enlarge their kingdom.

5. Ivan III was the first ruler to call himself __________ of a united Russian nation.

II. Rewrite the following false statements to make them true.

6. The Russians first settled *east* of the Ural Mountains, and ever since, the *Siberian* part of Russia has been the country's heartland.

7. In the early Middle Ages, the *Magyars* built a *cultural* center around the city of Kiev.

8. Moscow, located in the *southern steppe,* suffered little from the Mongol raids.

9. In 1328, the head of the *Greek* Orthodox Church made Moscow his permanent residence.

10. Hoping to increase Russia's trade with Europe, Ivan IV began a war to win free access to the *Black* Sea.

Name ______________________

Class ____________

Date ____________

Independent Practice Worksheet 12.1

Two great dynasties ruled China.
(pages 277–283)

For each event listed below, identify the dynasty in which it occurred and why it was an important event.

EVENT	DYNASTY	SIGNIFICANCE
1. The printing of paper money		
2. The conquest of Korea		
3. The annual payment of tribute to the Tatar khan		
4. The construction of the Grand Canal		
5. The rule of China by Wu-Chao		
6. The return of an examination system based on the teachings of Confucius		
7. The revolt of overworked and overtaxed peasants		
8. Trade in porcelain known for its delicacy and subtle colors		
9. The invention of movable type		
10. The invention of the compass	Sung	

Name ______________________

Class ____________

Date ____________

Independent Practice Worksheet 12.2

The Mongols conquered a vast empire.
(pages 283–287)

I. Complete the following sentences.

1. Between 1200 and 1350, the Mongol conquests extended from the ______________________ to the ______________________.

2. From 1229 to 1279 the Mongols conquered the ______________________ dynasty in Persia, the ______________________ kingdom in Russia, and the ______________________ dynasty in China.

3. Kublai Khan ruled China from Khanbalik, the site of modern-day ______________________.

4. The Mongols made the ______________________ safe from robbers and warring tribes.

5. The ______________________, ______________________, ______________________, and ______________________ were among the nomadic bands that originated in the steppes of Mongolia.

II. Who am I? Identify the speaker by placing the correct letter in the blank.

A. Genghis Khan B. Kublai Khan C. Marco Polo

____ 6. I placed many foreigners in high government positions.

____ 7. I was known as the Great Khan.

____ 8. I organized my armies into brigades.

____ 9. I overthrew the Sung dynasty.

____ 10. I attacked Japan.

____ 11. I told my stories while in prison.

____ 12. I spent my youth fighting for power on the Mongolian steppe.

____ 13. The tales of my travels were true, although many believed them to be tall tales.

____ 14. I became a trusted official in the Mongol government.

____ 15. I conquered most of Asia.

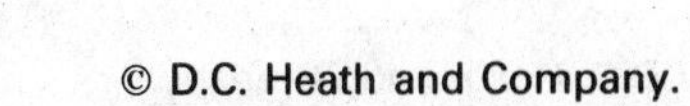

Name ____________________
Class ____________
Date ____________

Independent Practice Worksheet 12.3

China chose stability over change.
(pages 287–290)

Write a sentence that summarizes the main idea of each subsection in Section 3. The first one is done for you as an example.

The Ming dynasty brought peace.

Main idea: Chu Yüan-chang, the first Ming emperor, freed China from the Mongols and then brought all of China under his rule.

1. Ming scholars looked to the past.

____

____

____

2. The voyages of Cheng Ho marked a turning point in history.

____

____

____

3. The Ming dynasty collapsed.

____

____

____

4. A foreign dynasty took power.

____

____

____

Name ____________________
Class ____________
Date ____________

Independent Practice Worksheet 12.4

Japan developed a unique civilization.
(pages 290–294)

I. Listed below are terms and names associated with different periods in Japanese history. Place each in the correct time period. Some words may be associated with more than one time period.

arrival of Koreans, Buddhism, shoguns, Minamoto, clans, samurai, Kyoto, Yamato chiefs, Mongol invasion, emperors, Kamakura, nobles, the Shinto religion, Prince Shotoku, Chinese styles, pagodas, Heian, poetry, kana, Lady Murasaki Shikibu, feudalism, Nara, novels

1. about A.D. 300–500

____

____

2. about A.D. 500–800

____

____

3. about A.D. 800–1200

____

____

4. after A.D. 1200

____

____

II. Use these groups of events and other information in Section 4 to give a name to each time period.

5. about A.D. 300–500

____

6. about A.D. 500–800

____

7. about A.D. 800–1200

____

8. after A.D. 1200

____

Name ______________________
Class ______________
Date ______________

Independent Practice Worksheet 12.5

Japan turned to isolation.
(pages 294–297)

Complete the following sentences

1. After the decline of the Kamakura shoguns, feudal lords known as ______________________ became nearly independent rulers.
2. The years from 1467 to 1568 were known in Japan as the Age of the ______________________.
3. The first European ships arrived in Japan in ______________________.
4. The Japanese traded ______________________ for ______________________ with the first European merchants to reach their country.
5. The first Christian missionaries to enter Japan were members of the ______________________ Church.
6. Soon after the Europeans arrived, three rulers called ______________________, ______________________, and ______________________ tried to strengthen Japan's central government.
7. In 1614, Tokugawa Ieyasu banned ______________________ in Japan.
8. In the early 1600's all European merchants except the ______________________ were banned from trading in Japan.
9. As a result of Japan's isolation, it fell behind other countries in ______________________, ______________________, and ______________________.
10. Isolation gave Japan a long period of ______________________ and ______________________.
11. During the years of isolation, Buddhist monks developed a unique ______________________.
12. Zen Buddhists seek ______________________ enlightenment through ______________________.
13. Strict discipline of mind and body was the Zen path to ______________________.
14. Japanese paintings were for ______________________ and ______________________.
15. Nature played a key role in Japanese art and in ______________________.

Name ______________________
Class ____________
Date ____________

Independent Practice Worksheet 13.1

India flourished under the Guptas.
(pages 301–303)

Complete the outline of Section 1.

I. The Gupta dynasty ruled the north.
   A. Chandra Gupta was king of the upper Ganges valley.
   B. ______________________
   C. ______________________

II. Science and learning advanced.
   A. Education increased.
      1. Brahmins attended school from the ages of 9 to 30.
      2. ______________________
   B. There were many advances in the sciences.
      1. ______________________
      2. Surgery advanced.

III. Kalidasa wrote great drama.
   A. The greatest literature of India's golden age was drama.
   B. ______________________

IV. Huns destroyed the Gupta empire.
   A. ______________________
   B. ______________________

V. The Rajputs built new kingdoms.
   A. Northern India was divided into small kingdoms.
   B. The 800's and 900's were a great age of temple building.
   C. ______________________

VI. Hindus and Muslims met in war.
   A. Muslim Arabs conquered part of the Indus River valley in 712.
   B. ______________________

VII. Muslim sultans ruled from Delhi.
   A. ______________________
   B. ______________________

Name ____________________
Class ____________
Date ____________

Independent Practice Worksheet 13.2

Mughals ruled India in splendor.
(pages 304–308)

Give two facts about each of the following individuals.

1. Tamerlane

   a. ______________________________

   b. ______________________________

2. Babur

   a. ______________________________

   b. ______________________________

3. Akbar

   a. ______________________________

   b. ______________________________

4. Nur Jahan

   a. ______________________________

   b. ______________________________

5. Shah Jahan

   a. ______________________________

   b. ______________________________

6. Aurangzeb

   a. ______________________________

   b. ______________________________

7. Nanak

   a. ______________________________

   b. ______________________________

Name ______________________

Class ____________

Date ____________

Independent Practice Worksheet 13.3

Kingdoms arose in Southeast Asia.
(pages 309–311)

Listed below are effects. For each, list the possible causes.

1. *Effect:* Southeast Asia has never been united politically or culturally.
   Causes:

   a. ______________________

   b. ______________________

   c. ______________________

2. *Effect:* The key to political power in Southeast Asia has often been control of trade routes and harbors.
   Causes:

   a. ______________________

   b. ______________________

3. *Effect:* Indian influence spread to most areas of culture in Southeast Asia.
   Causes:

   a. ______________________

   b. ______________________

4. *Effect:* Between the 1200's and the 1400's, Muslim influence reached Southeast Asia.
   Causes:

   a. ______________________

   b. ______________________

Name ______________________

Class ____________

Date ____________

Independent Practice Worksheet 14.1

Kingdoms and city-states arose in East Africa.
(pages 315–320)

I. On a separate sheet of paper, rewrite the following false statements to make them true.

1. Africa is the third largest continent, exceeded in size only by North America and Europe.
2. As a result of their poor soil, the savannas are the most sparsely settled region in Africa.
3. The tsetse fly influenced African history by keeping invaders out of the savannas and by encouraging African farmers to import herds of cattle, donkeys, and horses.
4. Africa's shoreline encouraged contact with the outside world. Like Europe, Africa has a jagged coastline with many deep harbors.
5. The rising power of Zimbabwe played a crucial role in the fall of Meroë.

II. Fill in the word or words that correctly complete each statement.

6. The ______________________ is a desert that extends from the Atlantic Ocean to the Red Sea, covering an area roughly the size of the United States.
7. An ______________________ is a place where underground water comes to the surface in a spring or a well.
8. ______________________ is a process in which a semiarid region dries out and begins to turn to desert.
9. In 751 B.C., a ______________________ king named ______________________ led an army down the Nile and conquered Egypt.
10. In about A.D. 350, King ______________________ of ______________________ conquered Kush.
11. ______________________ is a culture formed from the blending of Arab and Bantu cultures.
12. The most common ships in a Swahili harbor were triangular-sailed Arab vessels called ______________________.
13. ______________________, ______________________, and ______________________ were three of the more than 35 city-states located along the East African coast.
14. The kingdom of Zimbabwe was located on a fertile plateau between the ______________________ and ______________________ rivers.
15. The name ______________________ is derived from a Bantu phrase meaning either "stone enclosure" or "dwelling of the chief."

Name ____________________
Class __________
Date __________

Independent Practice Worksheet 14.2

West African empires thrived on trade.
(pages 320–325)

I. Identify the West African empire described in each statement by placing the correct letter in the space provided.

A. Ghana B. Mali C. Songhai

____ 1. Muslim Berbers overran its northern borders in 1076.

____ 2. A Moroccan sultan named El Mansur conquered it in 1591.

____ 3. Only its king had the right to own gold nuggets.

____ 4. Its capital was Niami.

____ 5. One of its kings made a pilgrimage to Mecca.

____ 6. Its university at Timbuktu attracted Muslim scholars.

____ 7. Ibn Battuta visited it in 1352.

____ 8. It was the first of the great West African empires.

____ 9. Sunni Ali and Askia Muhammad ruled this empire.

____ 10. Sundiata gained control over this empire after defeating Sumangura.

II. In the space provided, write a brief definition for each of the following terms.

11. lineage: ____________________

12. matrilineal: ____________________

13. diviner: ____________________

14. polyrhythmic: ____________________

15. griot: ____________________

Name ______________________
Class ____________
Date ____________

Independent Practice Worksheet 14.3

Early Americans had many ways of life.
(pages 326–328)

I. Complete the following sentences.

1. The ______________________ and its tributaries drain a large, fertile plain in North America and provide it with ______________________.
2. The ______________________ contains more water than the next six largest rivers of the world combined.
3. During the most recent Ice Age, a ______________________ called Beringia connected Asia with North America.
4. America's earliest farmers lived in ______________________.
5. The people of Mexico and Central America called ____________ the food of the gods.

II. Identify the locations of the following cultural groups in North America.

6. Anasazi ______________________
7. Hopewell ______________________
8. Mississipian ______________________

III. Match each of the following statements with the cultural group it describes by placing the correct letter in the blank.

A. Anasazi B. Hopewell C. Mississipian

_____ 9. Cahokia was its largest and most important center.

_____ 10. It vanished after a prolonged drought.

_____ 11. They buried many of their finest products inside earthen mounds.

_____ 12. The Ohio River provided them with a central trade route.

_____ 13. Pueblo Bonito was their most important pueblo.

_____ 14. Their ruler announced the proper time for planting and harvesting crops.

_____ 15. A combination of wars, disease, and overpopulation ended their long period of prosperity.

_____ 16. They created a way of life that thrived from A.D. 600 to 1200.

_____ 17. Their sculptors carved stones into pipes shaped like falcons, beavers, and wildcats.

Name ________________

Class ________

Date ________

Independent Practice Worksheet 14.4

Great civilizations arose in the Americas. (pages 330–335)

I. Complete the following chart.

	Dates	Location	Achievement
1. Moche			
2. Inca			
3. Olmec			
4. Maya			
5. Aztec			

II. Use your chart to answer the following questions.

6. Which groups built empires in about the same time period? ________________
7. Which group had the largest empire? ________________
8. Which group or groups lived in North America? ________________
9. Which group or groups lived in South America? ________________
10. Which group or groups developed a calendar? ________________

Name ______________________

Class ____________

Date ____________

Independent Practice Worksheet 15.1

The Renaissance began in northern Italy.
(pages 345–349)

I. Complete the following lists.

1. List three characteristics that set the Renaissance apart from the Middle Ages.

a. ______________________________

b. ______________________________

c. ______________________________

2. List at least eight attributes of the ideal man, according to a book called *The Courtier.*

a. ______________ e. ______________

b. ______________ f. ______________

c. ______________ g. ______________

d. ______________ h. ______________

3. List at least eight attributes of the ideal woman, according to a book called *The Courtier.*

a. ______________ e. ______________

b. ______________ f. ______________

c. ______________ g. ______________

d. ______________ h. ______________

II. Who am I? Match each individual with his or her accomplishments.

A. Giotto di Bondone
B. Francesco Petrarch
C. Isabella d'Este
D. Dante Alighieri
E. Leon Battista Alberti

____ 4. I was famous for my art collection and my skill in politics. I ruled Mantua.

____ 5. I was an architect, an athlete, and a musician.

____ 6. I imitated the style of Cicero and strove for the classical virtues of simplicity and purity.

____ 7. My writings were a bridge between the Middle Ages and the Renaissance.

____ 8. My frescoes began a revolution in art.

Name ____________________

Class ____________

Date ____________

Independent Practice Worksheet 15.2

Florence led the way in arts.

(pages 350–353)

I. Complete the following sentences.

1. Florentines acquired their wealth through ____________________ and ____________________.

2. By the 1300's, Florence was the ____________________ center of Europe.

3. The ____________________ family came to power at the beginning of the golden age of Florence.

4. Cosimo Medici built the first ____________________ in western Europe.

5. Lorenzo Medici kept the good will of the common people by sponsoring ____________________, ____________________, ____________________, and ____________________.

II. Who am I? Match the artist with the appropriate descriptions.

A. Lorenzo Ghiberti
B. Donatello
C. Niccolo Machiavelli
D. Brunelleschi
E. Masaccio

____ 6. I capped a local cathedral with a gigantic dome.

____ 7. I developed perspective as a technique.

____ 8. I was trained as a goldsmith.

____ 9. I am considered the father of modern painting.

____ 10. I sculpted freestanding statues like those of the Greeks and Romans.

____ 11. I wrote a book called *The Prince.*

____ 12. I created two bronze doors for the cathedral's baptistry.

____ 13. I am famous for my statues of heroic figures on horseback.

____ 14. I was trained as an architect.

____ 15. I tried to understand why one ruler succeeded and another failed.

Name ____________________
Class ____________
Date ____________

Independent Practice Worksheet 15.3

The Renaissance spread.
(pages 354–358)

I. Identify each artist by placing the correct letter in the blank.

A. Michelangelo Buonarroti

B. Raphael Santi

C. Leonardo da Vinci

____ 1. born in 1475 in Caprese, Italy, and died in 1564 in Rome, Italy

____ 2. especially known for painting madonnas

____ 3. painted "the first distinctly psychological portrait of the Renaissance"

____ 4. sculpted the *Pieta*

____ 5. was the favorite painter of Pope Leo X

____ 6. painted the private library of Pope Julius II

____ 7. kept notebooks filled with new inventions, observations, and ideas

____ 8. sculpted a 16-foot statue of David

____ 9. died in 1520 when he was only 37

____ 10. painted the *Mona Lisa*

____ 11. painted the ceiling of the Sistine Chapel

____ 12. painted figures of classical and Renaissance times together

____ 13. was a scientist as well as an artist

____ 14. designed the dome for the new St. Peter's Cathedral

____ 15. experimented with bicycles, hydraulics, and masonry

II. List three characteristics of the Northern Renaissance.

16. ____

17. ____

18. ____

Name ______________________

Class ____________

Date ____________

Independent Practice Worksheet 15.4

Explorers discovered new lands.
(pages 358–364)

I. Complete the following lists.

1. List three factors that encouraged Europeans to search for new routes to Asia.

   a. ______________________

   b. ______________________

   c. ______________________

2. List the three inventions that allowed open sea travel for the Europeans.

   a. ______________________

   b. ______________________

   c. ______________________

II. Complete the following chart.

Explorer	Country sailed from	Dates of exploration	Area explored	Significance of exploration
3. Bartholomeu Dias				
4. Vasco da Gama				
5. Christopher Columbus				
6. Vasco Nuñez de Balboa				
7. Pedro Alvares Cabral				
8. Ferdinand Magellan				

Name ____________________

Class ____________

Date ____________

Independent Practice Worksheet 15.5

Other countries started colonies in America.
(pages 365–369)

I. In the space provided, write the name of the person who might have made each of the following statements.

____________________ 1. "I discovered what today is New York Harbor."

____________________ 2. "My voyage up the St. Lawrence River became the basis for France's claim to New France."

____________________ 3. "I founded the colony at Quebec."

____________________ 4. "I claimed Louisiana for France."

____________________ 5. "I discovered Newfoundland and claimed it for England."

____________________ 6. "I organized an expedition that tried to plant a colony on Roanoke Island."

____________________ 7. "I was the first governor of the Massachusetts Bay Colony."

____________________ 8. "I discovered the Hudson River."

II. Complete the following statements.

9. In the summer of 1673, a fur trader named ____________________ and a priest named ____________________ set out to discover if the Mississippi River offered the long-sought northwest passage.

10. The Puritans are called ____________________ because their views differed from those of the established church.

11. Before the Spanish came, the deadly germs of ____________________, and ____________________, and ____________________ were unknown in the Americas.

12. The sudden, rapid spread of disease to a large number of people is called an ____________________.

13. The ____________________, a staple of the Inca diet, was transported in European ships to almost every part of the Eastern Hemisphere.

14. Modern historians estimate that for every ____________________ Africans sold in the Americas, at least ____________________ others died on the way there.

15. European explorers hoped to find a ____________________ ____________________ through North America to Asia.

Name ______________________
Class ____________
Date ____________

Independent Practice Worksheet 16.1

Martin Luther began a religious revolt.
(pages 373–379)

List the supporting facts for each of the following generalizations.

1. *Generalization:* During the Renaissance, popes and other church leaders had many worldly concerns that left them with little time for spiritual duties.
   Facts:

   a. Popes patronized the arts and collected ancient manuscripts.

   b. ______________________

   c. ______________________

2. *Generalization:* Many people were devoutly religious.
   Facts:

   a. ______________________

   b. ______________________

   c. ______________________

3. *Generalization:* The rise in literacy and the invention of the printing press prepared the way for a religious revolution.
   Facts:

   a. ______________________

   b. ______________________

   c. ______________________

4. *Generalization:* The pope and the emperor tried to silence Luther but failed to do so.
   Facts:

   a. ______________________

   b. ______________________

   c. ______________________

5. *Generalization:* Luther's ideas were popular with many Germans.
   Facts:

   a. ______________________

   b. ______________________

   c. ______________________

Name ____________________

Class ____________

Date ____________

Independent Practice Worksheet 16.2

Protestantism spread in northern Europe.
(pages 379–383)

Identify when each of the following events took place. Then explain why the event was important.

1. The pope refused to end the marriage of Henry VIII to Catherine of Aragon.

   Date: ____________________ *Importance:* ____________________

   ____

   ____

2. England's Parliament approved the Act of Supremacy.

   Date: ____________________ *Importance:* ____________________

   ____

   ____

3. John Calvin published a book called the *Institutes of the Christian Religion.*

   Date: ____________________ *Importance:* ____________________

   ____

   ____

4. The people of Geneva asked John Calvin to lead their community.

   Date: ____________________ *Importance:* ____________________

   ____

   ____

5. Protestant nobles led by John Knox overthrew Mary Stuart.

   Date: ____________________ *Importance:* ____________________

   ____

   ____

6. Sweden revolted against the Danish King.

   Date: ____________________ *Importance:* ____________________

   ____

   ____

Name ______________________

Class ____________

Date ____________

Independent Practice Worksheet 16.3

The Catholic Church made reforms.
(pages 384–386)

Give at least two effects of each of the following events.

1. In 1540, the pope made Ignatius's band of followers a new monastic order called the Society of Jesus, or as it was more commonly known, the Jesuits.
   Effects:

   a. ____

   b. ____

2. In 1545, Catholic bishops and cardinals met in the town of Trent.
   Effects:

   a. ____

   b. ____

3. In 1559, Pope Paul IV drew up a list of books that he considered dangerous to the Catholic faith.
   Effects:

   a. ____

   b. ____

4. In 1544, Holy Roman Emperor Charles V took up arms against the Protestant princes of Germany.
   Effects:

   a. ____

   b. ____

5. In 1555, the Peace of Augsburg was signed.
   Effects:

   a. ____

   b. ____

Name ______________________
Class ____________
Date ____________

Independent Practice Worksheet 16.4

Scientists challenged old assumptions.
(pages 386–389)

Identify the contribution to science made by each of the following individuals.

1. Nicholas Copernicus

____

____

2. Johannes Kepler

____

____

3. Galileo Galilei

a. ____

b. ____

c. ____

4. Andreas Vesalius

____

5. William Harvey

____

6. Zacharias Janssen

____

7. Anton van Leeuwenhoek

____

8. Gabriel Fahrenheit

____

9. Anders Celsius

____

10. Evangelista Torricelli

____

Name ____________________
Class ____________
Date ____________

Independent Practice Worksheet 17.1

Spain built an overseas empire.
(pages 393–397)

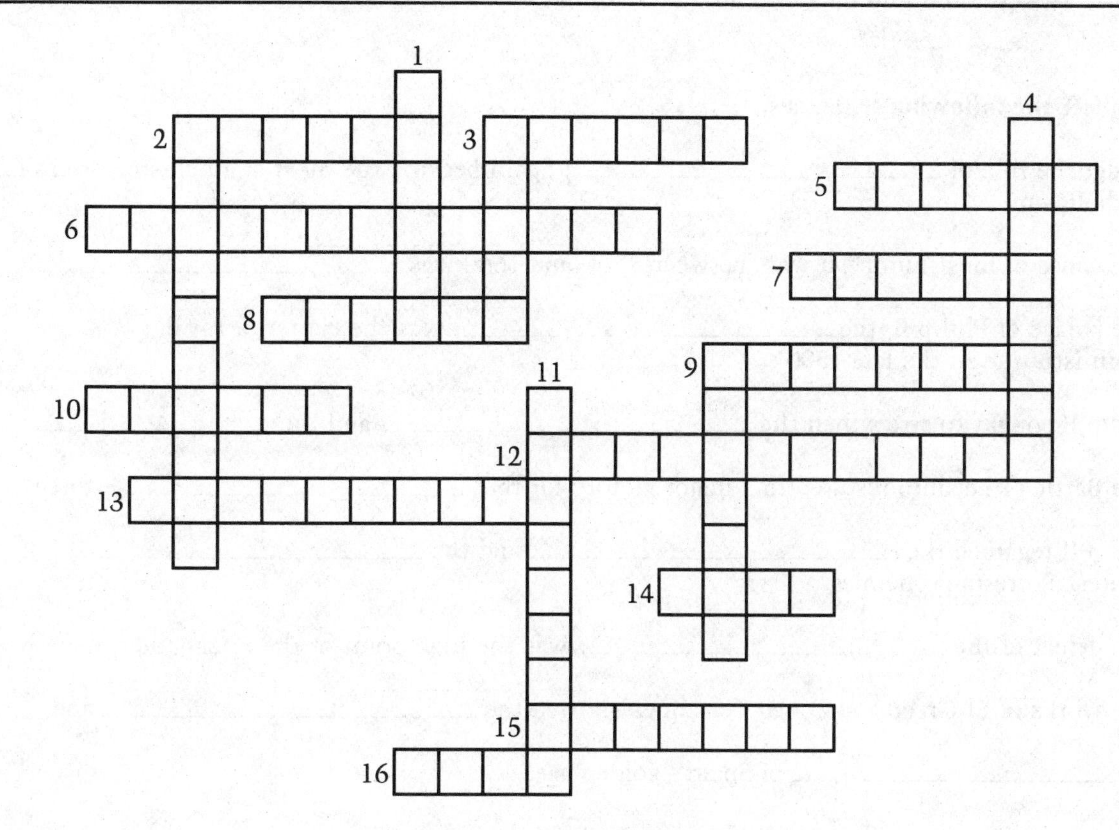

ACROSS

2. Sailed north from Cuba in 1539 in search of riches
3. At first, they believed Cortés was a god.
5. She helped to conquer Chile.
6. Daring Spanish fortune hunters
7. What Cortés and Pizarro found
8. The most northern point Coronado explored
9. He helped to conquer Chile.
10. One of Cortés's advantages over the Aztecs
12. The capital of the Aztecs
13. The privilege that the Council of the Indies granted certain settlers
14. Atahualpa offered it as part of his ransom.
15. Conquered the Incas
16. The capital of Peru

DOWN

1. Conquered the Aztecs
2. Helped Cortés by translating for him and advising him
3. Where the Inca empire lay
4. The name of Spain's North American territories
9. The royal agent of the king of Spain in the Americas
11. The Inca ruler

Name ____________________
Class __________
Date __________

Independent Practice Worksheet 17.2

Spain was a Catholic bulwark.
(pages 398–401)

I. Complete the following sentences.

1. Under the rule of ____________________, Spain became the most staunch supporter of Catholicism.

2. The cause of most European wars between 1560 and 1660 was ____________________.

3. The palace of Philip II, the ____________________, was the center of royal administration in the late 1500's.

4. Philip II sought to strengthen the ____________________ and the ____________________.

5. The Battle of Lepanto resulted in a major victory for the ____________________ forces.

6. Philip II regarded the ____________________ and the ____________________ as his greatest Protestant enemies.

7. The defeat of the ____________________ was the high point of the Elizabethan Age.

8. The works of El Greco and Diego Velázquez showed the ____________________ and ____________________ of Spain's golden age.

9. The two major economic problems in Spain in 1650 were ____________________ and ____________________.

10. The Spanish imported many of the goods they needed from ____________________, ____________________, and ____________________.

II. Rewrite the following false statements to make them true.

11. Philip II extended his borders by taking *northern Italy.*

12. In Philip II's eyes, Catholicism had two rivals, *the king of France* and *the ruler of Venice.*

13. Elizabeth I's open support for *Spanish* rebels and her encouragement of the *English navy* led her into conflict with *France.*

14. Miguel de Cervantes' novel was a satire on *serfdom.*

15. In the first half of the 1600's, Spain suffered *deflation* as gold and silver flowed *into* the Americas.

Name ______________________

Class ____________

Date ____________

Independent Practice Worksheet 17.3

The Netherlands won independence.
(pages 402–406)

I. Identify the following individuals and tell why each was important to the Netherlands.

1. Margaret of Spain

   Who? ______________________

   Why important? ______________________

2. Duke of Alva

   Who? ______________________

   Why important? ______________________

3. Prince William of Orange

   Who? ______________________

   Why important? ______________________

II. Tell how each of the following helped the Netherlands to prosper and grow.

4. capitalism

   Identify ______________________

   Why important? ______________________

5. Amsterdam Exchange Bank

   Identify ______________________

   Why important? ______________________

6. Dutch East Indies Company

   Identify ______________________

   Why important? ______________________

Name ______________
Class ______________
Date ______________

Independent Practice Worksheet 17.4

France's crown changed hands.
(pages 406–411)

List the main idea of each subsection in Section 4.

1. Catherine de Medici ruled France.

   Main Idea: ______________________________

2. The Valois dynasty ended.

   Main Idea: ______________________________

3. Henry IV brought peace.

   Main Idea: ______________________________

4. Cardinal Richelieu controlled France.

   Main Idea: ______________________________

5. French thinkers questioned authority.

   Main Idea: ______________________________

Name ____________________

Class __________

Date __________

Independent Practice Worksheet 17.5

Religious wars split Germany.
(pages 410–411)

For each event, state the most significant effect.

1. Ferdinand II became king of Bohemia. *Effect:* ____________________

2. The Czechs revolted against the rule of Ferdinand II. *Effect:* ____________________

3. Ferdinand sent an army to crush the Czechs. *Effect:* ____________________

4. Several German Protestant princes challenged Ferdinand II. *Effect:* ____________________

5. Richelieu feared the Hapsburgs. *Effect:* ____________________

6. The Thirty Years' War, which began in 1618, finally ended in 1648. *Effect:* ____________________

7. The Treaty of Westphalia marked the end of the Thirty Years' War.

   Effects:

   a. ____________________

   b. ____________________

   c. ____________________

Name ____________________
Class ____________
Date ____________

Independent Practice Worksheet 18.1

Elizabeth I faced many challenges.
(pages 421–425)

In the late 1500's, England faced grave challenges from four directions at once. Identify each challenge and its cause or causes. Then explain how Elizabeth I helped England to meet that challenge.

1. Religious divisions
   a. The problem: ____________________
   b. The cause or causes: ____________________
   ____
   c. Elizabeth's solution ____________________
2. Mary Stuart, Queen of Scots
   a. The problem: ____________________
   b. The cause or causes: ____________________
   ____
   c. Elizabeth's solution ____________________
3. Philip of Spain
   a. The problem: ____________________
   b. The cause or causes: ____________________
   ____
   c. Elizabeth's solution ____________________
4. Financial difficulties
   a. The problem: ____________________
   b. The cause or causes: ____________________
   ____
   c. Elizabeth's solution ____________________

Name ____________________
Class __________
Date __________

Independent Practice Worksheet 18.2

The Elizabethan era was a golden age.
(pages 426–429)

I. Mark an *A* beside all of the following statements that accurately describe London in the late 1500's and early 1600's.

____ 1. The English Channel separated London from the rest of England.

____ 2. Beards were outlawed in London.

____ 3. Boats were the fastest means of transportation in the city.

____ 4. London streets were wide and safe.

____ 5. Londoners enjoyed the theater.

____ 6. London lacked plumbing.

____ 7. London was densely populated.

____ 8. Houses in London had spacious yards.

____ 9. Most Londoners were middle-class citizens.

____ 10. London Bridge had fallen down.

____ 11. Physical mutilation was a frequent punishment for criminals.

____ 12. The Thames River ran through London.

____ 13. London had a hoard of petty criminals.

____ 14. Everyone over seven years of age wore a hat on Sundays and on holidays.

____ 15. Its walls enclosed a space only one mile square.

II. Complete the following sentences.

16. In England, a burst of pride and self confidence surfaced after the English defeated ______________.

17. The props of the English theater included ______________________, ______________________, ______________________, ______________________, and ______________________.

18. William Shakespeare displayed his great genius as both a ______________ and a ______________.

19. Shakespeare's plays were often performed at the ______________________ Theater.

20. The first permanent theater was built in ______________________ by ______________________.

Name ____________________

Class ____________

Date ____________

Independent Practice Worksheet 18.3

England had a civil war.
(pages 430–434)

Identify the outcome of each of the following actions.

1. James I and Charles I were in constant need of money.

2. In 1628, the king called Parliament into session to ask for new taxes.

3. In 1639, William Laud ordered Charles's Presbyterian subjects in Scotland to follow the Church of England's style of worship.

4. The Scots gathered a huge army and threatened to invade England.

5. Throughout the autumn of 1641, Parliament passed laws limiting Charles's power.

6. Charles fled to the north to raise an army.

7. Cromwell's New Model Army defeated the king's forces.

8. Cromwell and the Puritans brought Charles to trial for treason.

Name ____________________
Class ____________
Date ____________

Independent Practice Worksheet 18.4

Parliament won political power.
(pages 434–437)

I. Complete the following sentences.

1. In 1660, Parliament invited ____________________ to return from exile.
2. The period of rule by Charles II is known as the ____________________.
3. The Habeas Corpus Act gave a prisoner the right to ____________________.
4. The two issues that haunted Charles II as much as they haunted his father and grandfather were ____________________ and ____________________.
5. When Charles died, the throne of England would pass to ____________________.
6. The ancestors of England's first political parties were the ____________________ and the ____________________.
7. Three events in the reign of James II that excited the fears of English Protestants were ____________________, ____________________, and ____________________.
8. The overthrow of James II is known as the ____________________.
9. In 1689, Parliament asked William and Mary to rule England as ____________________.
10. The English Bill of Rights prohibits a ruler from ____________________, ____________________, ____________________, ____________________, ____________________, ____________________, and ____________________.

II. Match each person to the ideas that he is associated with.

A. John Locke B. Thomas Hobbes

_____ 11. People are naturally wicked.

_____ 12. People have the gift of reason.

_____ 13. The purpose of government is to protect rights to life, liberty, and property.

_____ 14. The purpose of government is to protect people from their own selfishness.

_____ 15. The best government is an absolute monarchy.

Name ______________
Class ______________
Date ______________

Independent Practice Worksheet 19.1

The Sun King ruled France.
(pages 441–447)

I. Who am I? Identify each of the following individuals by placing the appropriate letter in the blank.

____ 1. Cardinal Richelieu

____ 2. Louis XIV

____ 3. Jean Baptiste Lully

____ 4. Cardinal Mazarin

____ 5. Jean Baptiste Colbert

____ 6. Jean Baptiste Racine

____ 7. Molière

____ 8. Philip V of Spain

A. Louis XIV's minister of finance

B. chief musician to Louis XIV

C. the power behind the throne of Louis XIII

D. negotiated the Treaty of Westphalia

E. author of biting satires on French society

F. dramatist who specialized in tragedy

G. king at age five

H. grandson of Louis XIV

II. Explain the connection between each of the following pairs.

9. mercantilism and the Huguenots ______________

____

____

10. France's economy and the revoking of the Edict of Nantes ______________

____

____

11. Versailles and Louis XIV ______________

____

____

12. the Treaty of Utrecht and the balance of power in Europe ______________

____

____

Name ______________________
Class ____________
Date ____________

Independent Practice Worksheet 19.2

Peter the Great changed Russia.
(pages 447–452)

I. Tell when each of the following events took place.

1. Peter I came to the throne.

2. Peter I signed a peace treaty with Finland and Sweden.

3. Peter I visited western Europe.

4. Peter I died.

5. Peter I abolished the office of patriarch.

6. The Romanovs came to power.

7. The Great Northern War began.

8. The city of Azov fell to the Russians.

9. The Swedes invaded the Ukraine.

10. Peter I took full power in his own name.

11. Building began on a new capital for Russia.

12. The czar proclaimed St. Petersburg the new capital of Russia.

II. Place the events listed in Part I in chronological order, beginning with the number of the earliest event.

____

____

Name ____________________
Class ____________
Date ____________

Independent Practice Worksheet 19.3

Austria and Prussia rose to power.
(pages 452–457)

For each statement, provide the appropriate supporting facts.

1. Central Europe around 1700 was dominated by three weakening empires.

   a. ____________________

   b. ____________________

   c. ____________________

2. The power of the Hapsburgs remained strong in the 1700's.

   a. ____________________

   b. ____________________

3. The Hohenzollerns built up their state.

   a. ____________________

   b. ____________________

   c. ____________________

4. The Prussian army grew in strength during the first half of the eighteenth century.

   a. ____________________

   b. ____________________

   c. ____________________

5. Frederick II successfully invaded the Hapsburg lands.

   a. ____________________

   b. ____________________

6. As national interests changed, alliances in Europe shifted.

   a. ____________________

   b. ____________________

   c. ____________________

Name ____________________

Class ____________

Date ____________

Independent Practice Worksheet 20.1

European thinkers expressed new ideas.
(pages 461–466)

For each individual listed below, identify his or her contributions to the world and the impact of those contributions. Two samples are done for you.

	Contributions	Impact
1. Isaac Newton		started people investigating everything in nature
2. Voltaire	philosophical writings, *Candide*	
3. Denis Diderot		
4. Joseph Priestley and Antoine Lavoisier		
5. Benjamin Franklin		
6. James Cook		
7. Johann Sebastian Bach and George Frederick Handel		
8. Franz Joseph Haydn		
9. Wolfgang Amadeus Mozart		
10. Ludwig van Beethoven		

Name ______________________
Class ____________
Date ____________

Independent Practice Worksheet 20.2

Writers advocated liberty and reason.
(pages 466–468)

ACROSS

2. Wrote *On the Spirit of Laws*
4. Division of power into three branches (3 words)
5. The kind of trade Adam Smith favored
7. The kinds of power lawmakers hold
10. The kind of power a ruler and his or her advisors hold
13. Declared, "Man is born free, yet everywhere he is in chains"
14. It and demand determine price.

DOWN

1. Rousseau's best-known book on government (3 words)
3. Wrote *The Wealth of Nations*
4. What Adam Smith believed that people work for (2 words)
6. What a good society allows, according to the philosophes
8. It and quantity available determine price.
9. The kind of power judges hold
11. One who believes in laissez faire
12. According to Rousseau, it and liberty exist in the state of nature.

Name ______________________

Class ______________

Date ______________

Independent Practice Worksheet 20.3

Enlightened despots sought progress.
(pages 469–472)

Complete the following lists.

1. List six actions or ideas of Frederick II that represented the spirit of the Enlightenment.

   a. ______________________________

   b. ______________________________

   c. ______________________________

   d. ______________________________

   e. ______________________________

   f. ______________________________

2. List six actions or ideas of Catherine the Great that represented the spirit of the Enlightenment.

   a. ______________________________

   b. ______________________________

   c. ______________________________

   d. ______________________________

   e. ______________________________

   f. ______________________________

3. List three actions that suggest Frederick II did not accept all the ideas of the Enlightenment.

   a. ______________________________

   b. ______________________________

   c. ______________________________

4. List three actions that suggest Catherine did not accept all the ideas of the Enlightenment.

   a. ______________________________

   b. ______________________________

   c. ______________________________

Name ______________________

Class ____________

Date ____________

Independent Practice Worksheet 20.4

Britain developed new forms of leadership.
(pages 472–475)

I. Complete the following sentences.

1. After 1688, Britain had a ______________________ in which the power of the ruler was limited by law.

2. An executive committee that acts in the ruler's name but in reality represents the majority party of Parliament is called a ______________________.

3. George I and his son George II relied heavily on ______________________.

4. In the early 1700's, the center of power and policymaking was ______________________.

5. Robert Walpole was the first person to act as a ______________________, although he did not use the title.

6. In the early 1700's, only about ____________ percent of Britain's population could vote, and the ______________________ ran the government.

7. In the 1700's, much of Britain's energy was directed toward ______________________ an empire.

8. The most valuable part of Britain's North American empire was ______________________.

9. According to mercantilists, colonies existed to ______________________.

10. Parliament passed the Stamp Act because it wanted its American colonists to ______________________.

II. Change each of the following false statements to make it true.

11. The *Stamp Act* is a good example of mercantilist policy.

12. The *people* of Britain elected members of the House of Commons.

13. For 20 years, from 1721 to 1741, *George II* was the unofficial ruler of Great Britain.

14. Since Whigs held a majority of seats in the House of Commons, William decided that his cabinet ministers should be *Tories*.

15. In the eighteenth century, Britain was a *democracy*.

Name ____________
Class ____________
Date ____________

Independent Practice Worksheet 20.5

Americans created a republic.
(pages 475–479)

I. Indicate the most significant effect of each of the following events.

1. The British passed an import tax on tea.

   Effect: ____________

2. Americans dumped 342 chests of tea into Boston Harbor.

   Effect: ____________

3. In September 1774, representatives from every colony except Georgia protested the treatment of Boston and sent a list of complaints to George III.

   Effect: ____________

4. British soldiers and American militiamen opened fire at each other on Lexington green.

   Effect: ____________

II. Complete the following lists.

5. List five factors that helped the Americans win their war for independence.

   a. ____________

   b. ____________

   c. ____________

   d. ____________

   e. ____________

6. List three political theories of the Enlightenment that are reflected in the Constitution.

   a. ____________

   b. ____________

   c. ____________

Name ______________________

Class ____________

Date ____________

Independent Practice Worksheet 21.1

The French monarchy faced a crisis.
(pages 483–487)

I. Indicate the estate to which an individual who engaged in each of the following vocations would most likely have belonged.

A. First Estate B. Second Estate C. Third Estate

____ 1. Lawyer

____ 2. Abbot

____ 3. Government officeholder

____ 4. Manufacturer

____ 5. Servant

____ 6. General

____ 7. Peasant

____ 8. Peddler

____ 9. Court officer

____ 10. Tanner

____ 11. Weaver

____ 12. Merchant

____ 13. Cook

____ 14. Archbishop

____ 15. Doctor

____ 16. Shopkeeper

____ 17. Bishop

____ 18. Brewer

____ 19. Parish priest

____ 20. Butcher

II. Indicate the estate or estates to which the following statements refer by placing the correct letter or letters in the blank.

A. First Estate B. Second Estate C. Third Estate

____ 21. made up more than 95 percent of the population

____ 22. paid a household tax

____ 23. owned about 10 percent of the land

____ 24. adopted the ideas of Abbe Sieyes

____ 25. dominated the Estates General in the Middle Ages

____ 26. demanded that all three estates meet together in 1789

____ 27. demanded that individual votes of the members in the three estates count equally

____ 28. made up less than 2 percent of the population

____ 29. paid taxes to the king's agent

____ 30. expected to dominate the Estates General in 1789

Name ______________________

Class ____________

Date ____________

Independent Practice Worksheet 21.2

Revolution brought reform and terror.
(pages 487–491)

I. Place the following events in chronological order, beginning with the earliest event.

____

1. Moderate leaders of the National Convention drafted a new constitution.
2. Louis and his family tried to escape from France.
3. The Legislative Assembly declared war on Austria.
4. The Directory governed France.
5. Enemy armies were advancing toward Paris.
6. The National Convention took office.
7. The National Assembly adopted *A Declaration of the Rights of Man and of the Citizen.*
8. Louis was beheaded.
9. The National Convention drafted 300,000 men into the army.

10. The National Assembly completed a new constitution.
11. Robespierre formed the Committee of Public Safety.
12. Members of the National Convention turned on Robespierre.
13. The Legislative Assembly took office.
14. The Legislative Assembly abolished the monarchy and declared France a republic.
15. Britain, Spain, and Portugal joined Prussia and Austria in an alliance known as the First Coalition.

II. Study the list of events above and then place them in the correct category. Not every event will be used, and some events may be fit into more than one category.

16. Events that made France a more democratic country ______________________
17. Events that made France less democratic ______________________
18. Events that threatened France's security ______________________
19. Events that increased France's security ______________________
20. Events that showed that France had experienced a revolution ______________________

Name ______________________

Class ______________

Date ______________

Independent Practice Worksheet 21.3

Napoleon conquered much of Europe.
(pages 492–495)

I. Tell how each of the following events helped Napoleon rise to power.

1. In 1795, an army of royalists threatened the palace where the National Convention met.

____

2. In 1796, the Directory appointed Bonaparte to command a French army against Austria and the Kingdom of Sardinia.

____

3. By 1799, the Directory had lost the confidence of the French people.

____

4. In 1799, the Second Coalition threatened France.

____

5. In 1800, the French voted overwhelmingly for Bonaparte's constitution.

____

II. Complete the following lists.

6. List four ways in which Napoleon restored order to France.

   a. ____

   b. ____

   c. ____

   d. ____

7. List three changes from the Revolution that Napoleon kept.

   a. ____

   b. ____

   c. ____

Name ____________________
Class ____________
Date ____________

Independent Practice Worksheet 21.4

Napoleon's empire collapsed.
(pages 496–499)

I. Give one reason or cause for each of the following events.

1. Napoleon cut off all trade with Britain.

   Why? ____

   ____

2. Bands of Spanish guerrillas struck at French forces in Spain.

   Why? ____

   ____

3. Napoleon decided to invade Russia.

   Why? ____

   ____

4. Alexander I burned Moscow.

   Why? ____

   ____

5. Britain, Russia, Prussia, Austria, and Sweden formed the Grand Alliance against Napoleon.

   Why? ____

   ____

II. Complete the following sentences.

6. Napoleon's ban on trade with Britain was known as the ____________________.
7. Napoleon's fight against the Spanish guerrillas is called the ____________________.
8. Napoleon's army was weakened by the ____________________ policy of the Russians.
9. In 1814, Napoleon gave up his throne, and his enemies gave him a small pension and exiled him to ____________________.
10. Napoleon's last bid for power is called ____________________ and ended with his defeat at the ____________________.

Name ______________________

Class __________

Date __________

Independent Practice Worksheet 22.1

Many factors aided industrial growth.
(pages 509–511)

Tell how each of the following factors helped to bring about the Industrial Revolution in eastern England and southern Scotland.

1. Changes in farming

   a. ______________________________

   b. ______________________________

2. A rise in population

   a. ______________________________

   b. ______________________________

3. Abundant national resources

   ____

   ____

4. A favorable location

   ____

   ____

5. A favorable climate for new ideas

   ____

   ____

6. The banking system

   ____

   ____

7. Political stability

   a. ______________________________

   b. ______________________________

Name ______________________

Class ____________

Date ____________

Independent Practice Worksheet 22.2

Britain led in the rise of industry.
(pages 511–514)

I. Identify the invention, the date it was developed, and the inventor.

1. This invention allowed weavers to work twice as fast.

   Invention: ______________ Date: ______________ Inventor: ______________

2. This invention allowed a spinner to work with six or eight threads at a time.

   Invention: ______________ Date: ______________ Inventor: ______________

3. This invention used waterpower to drive spinning wheels.

   Invention: ______________ Date: ______________ Inventor: ______________

4. This invention produced stronger, finer, and more even thread.

   Invention: ______________ Date: ______________ Inventor: ______________

5. This invention restored the balance between the thread makers and the weavers.

   Invention: ______________ Date: ______________ Inventor: ______________

6. This invention allowed cotton growers to keep up with spinners and weavers.

   Invention: ______________ Date: ______________ Inventor: ______________

II. Answer the following questions.

7. Which inventions led to the growth of factories?

   ____

8. Why did the inventions you identified above help factories to grow?

   ____

9. Why were the first factories located near rushing water?

   ____

10. What invention allowed factories to be located anywhere?

   ____

Name ______________________

Class __________

Date __________

Independent Practice Worksheet 22.3

Industry grew and spread to new lands.
(pages 514–518)

Complete the following lists.

1. List three changes in transportation in the 1700's.

   a. ______________________

   b. ______________________

   c. ______________________

2. List four effects of rail transportation.

   a. ______________________

   ____

   b. ______________________

   ____

   c. ______________________

   ____

   d. ______________________

   ____

3. List five countries to which the Industrial Revolution had spread by 1850.

   a. ______________________

   b. ______________________

   c. ______________________

   d. ______________________

   e. ______________________

4. List four reasons Great Britain was the leading industrial nation in 1850.

   a. ______________________

   b. ______________________

   c. ______________________

   d. ______________________

Name ____________________

Class ____________

Date ____________

Independent Practice Worksheet 22.4

Industry changed ways of life.
(pages 519–523)

Answer the following questions as if you were a person living in the nineteenth century.

1. (a) You are a resident of an English industrial city in the early 1800's. What improvements would make your city a better place to live?

   ____

   ____

   (b) How would you seek to implement these changes?

   ____

   ____

2. (a) You are an adult working in an English factory in the early nineteenth century. What conditions would you want to change?

   ____

   ____

   (b) How would you seek to implement these changes?

   ____

   ____

3. (a) You are a child working in an English coal mine in the early nineteenth century. What conditions would you want to change?

   ____

   ____

   (b) As a child, how would you have been affected by the passage of the Factory Act in 1833?

   ____

   ____

Name ____________________

Class ____________

Date ____________

Independent Practice Worksheet 23.1

European leaders sought stability.
(pages 527–530)

For each statement, identify the group whose political philosophy it represented in the early 1800's. Some statements reflect the beliefs of more than one group.

C. Conservatives L. Liberals R. Radicals

____ 1. justified the Reign of Terror

____ 2. favored drastic and sometimes violent change

____ 3. believed that the best form of government was an absolute monarchy

____ 4. controlled Europe after the Congress of Vienna

____ 5. favored the ideals of the French Revolution

____ 6. liked the early reforms of the French Revolution

____ 7. wanted more power for elected assemblies

____ 8. protected traditional forms of government

____ 9. believed in the idea of a true democracy

____ 10. appealed to the bourgeoisie, business leaders, and merchants

____ 11. found support among the working classes and students

____ 12. wanted civil participation by educated property owners

____ 13. supported primarily by the upper class

____ 14. wanted elected Parliaments with voting rights for all the people

____ 15. believed that the French Revolution accomplished little or nothing

____ 16. feared mobs

____ 17. favored the principle of legitimacy

____ 18. had the support of Metternich

____ 19. committed to the ideals of liberty, fraternity, and equality

____ 20. believed that it was wrong to bar people from politics because they were not of noble birth

Name ____________________
Class __________
Date __________

Independent Practice Worksheet 23.2

New ideals affected politics and art.
(pages 531–535)

I. Match each statement to the appropriate country or countries.

A. Greece B. France C. Italy D. Austria E. Germany

_____ 1. It was the first country to become independent after the Congress of Vienna.

_____ 2. Its citizens flocked to the army to defend democracy.

_____ 3. Its harsh policies against nationalism created a climate for rebellion.

_____ 4. It was once under Ottoman rule.

_____ 5. Austria was an obstacle to its unity.

_____ 6. Its dominant national group was German, but it included many nationalities.

_____ 7. Its fight for independence won support from many educated Europeans.

_____ 8. Cultural differences divided its northern and southern sections.

_____ 9. Its conquests sparked nationalism in the conquered countries.

_____ 10. It was threatened by the new nationalism that followed the French Revolution.

II. Identify each of the following individuals in the space provided.

11. My real name was Amandine Aurore Dupin.

____

12. I used England's windswept moors for the setting of my novels.

____

13. I turned from tightly controlled music to music filled with emotion.

____

14. I believed that nature represented the highest good.

____

15. I wrote "my heart is my own, peculiar to itself."

____

Name ____________________

Class ____________

Date ____________

Independent Practice Worksheet 23.3

Latin America won independence.
(pages 535–540)

I. Complete the following chart.

	Leader or leaders of revolt	Date or dates of independence	Mother country	New rulers
1. Haiti				
2. Spanish South America				
3. Brazil				
4. Mexico				

II. Use the chart and your text to answer the following questions.

5. Which country or countries experienced the most radical change in government?

____

6. Which country or countries experienced only a change in kings?

____

7. Which country or countries was controlled by creoles?

____

8. Which country or countries was the first to win independence?

____

9. Which country or countries won independence without going to war?

____

10. In which country or countries did priests take a leading role in the fight for independence?

____

Name ____________________

Class __________

Date __________

Independent Practice Worksheet 23.4

Reform and revolution swept Europe.
(pages 541–543)

I. By placing the appropriate letter in the space provided, indicate the time period in which each of the following events took place.

	A		B		C		D		E	
1830		1835		1840		1845		1850		1855

____ 1. An almost bloodless revolution ended the rule of France's Charles X.

____ 2. Louis Napoleon dissolved the French parliament.

____ 3. A revolution broke out in the Kingdom of the Two Sicilies.

____ 4. The French drew up a constitution that called for a parliament and a popularly elected president.

____ 5. The British parliament passed a reform bill that gave nearly all middle class British males the right to vote.

II. Rearrange the following statements in chronological order.

____

6. Any Englishman who paid a certain amount of rent could vote.
7. Frederick William IV agreed to the election of a democratic parliament.
8. Charles X fled to England.
9. Metternich resigned and fled to England.
10. Louis Philippe was crowned king.
11. Louis Napoleon took the title of Napoleon III.
12. German princes recalled their representatives from Frankfurt.

Name ______________________
Class ____________
Date ____________

Independent Practice Worksheet 24.1

Industrialism created a global economy.
(pages 547–550)

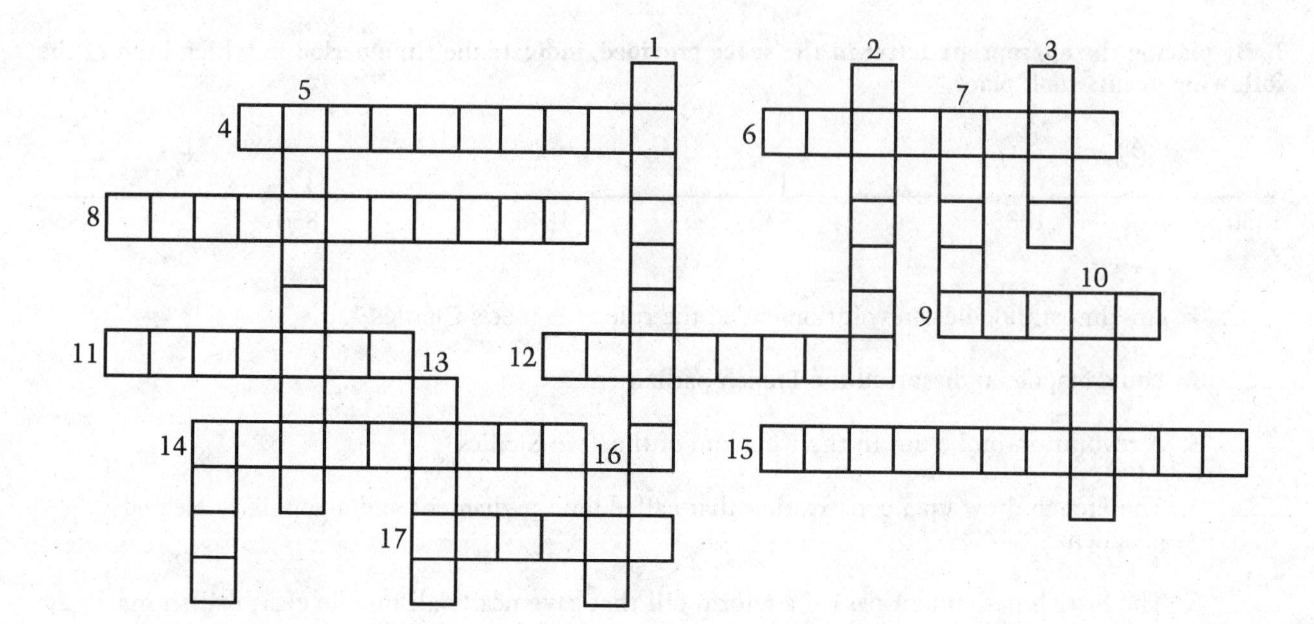

ACROSS

4. The act of leaving one's country to settle in another
6. Harbor at the north end of the Suez Canal
8. The movement of people to a new country
9. The inventor of the first successful telegraph
11. Money for investment
12. What Standard Oil was in the 1880's
14. Nickname for a train (2 words)
15. The speed at which telegraphs send information
17. A railroad passage that goes through a mountain

DOWN

1. A collapse in this industry led to a panic in 1857
2. British railroad tycoon
3. Source of power for most oceangoing vessels before 1870
5. The movement of people from one place to another
7. Source of power for 40 percent of oceangoing vessels after 1870
10. A share in a corporation
13. By how much the Suez Canal shortened travel time between Europe and India
14. The output of this resource increased fourfold worldwide between 1850 and 1875
16. Sea at the southern end of the Suez Canal

Name ______________________

Class __________

Date __________

Independent Practice Worksheet 24.2

Working people gained influence.
(pages 551–554)

Identify each of the following speakers. Some names will be used more than once.

1. I was labeled a utopian socialist by Karl Marx. ______________________
2. I supported the Marx family and was co-author of the *Communist Manifesto* and *Das Kapital*.

   ____
3. I attacked the middle class in my paintings. ______________________
4. I wrote realistic novels in Britain as did such writers as Thomas Hardy and William Thackeray.

   ____
5. I said that the only reason for the novel is that "it does attempt to represent life."

   ____
6. Along with Dostoevsky, I wrote realistic novels set in Russia. ______________________
7. Both Flaubert and I wrote realistic novels set in France. ______________________
8. Our work helped to start the Labour Party. ______________________
9. I broadened voting rights in France. ______________________
10. I ridiculed the romantics as "painters of angels." ______________________
11. I saw history as a class struggle. ______________________
12. I drew scathing pictures of pompous, self-satisfied individuals.

    ____
13. I believed that economics was the key to understanding the past and the present.

    ____
14. I tried to put my socialist ideals into practice.

    ____
15. I ruled a country that was the first in Europe to allow universal manhood suffrage.

    ____

Name ____________________

Class ____________

Date ____________

Independent Practice Worksheet 24.3

Italy and Germany formed nations.
(pages 555–561)

Provide evidence in support of each of the following statements.

1. Camillo di Cavour was a master of realpolitik.

   a. ____________________

   b. ____________________

   c. ____________________

   d. ____________________

2. Otto von Bismarck was a master of realpolitik.

   a. ____________________

   b. ____________________

   c. ____________________

3. The Franco-Prussian War strengthened Prussia.

   a. ____________________

   b. ____________________

   c. ____________________

4. The Franco-Prussian War weakened France and led to internal crises.

   a. ____________________

   b. ____________________

   c. ____________________

5. Between 1815 and 1871, the balance of power shifted in Europe.

   a. ____________________

   b. ____________________

   c. ____________________

Name ____________________
Class ____________
Date ____________

Independent Practice Worksheet 24.4

The United States spread westward.
(pages 561–565)

I. Rearrange the following statements in chronological order.

1. Mexico won its independence from Spain.
2. The United States added the Thirteenth Amendment to its Constitution.
3. Napoleon acquired the Louisiana Territory.
4. Confederate guns fired on Fort Sumter.
5. The United States had over 50,000 miles of railroad track.
6. California became a part of the United States.
7. The Mississippi River marked the western boundary of the United States.
8. Texas became an independent country.
9. The United States celebrated its hundredth anniversary.
10. The Confederate States of America was established.
11. Great Britain drove the French out of North America.
12. The Confederate army surrendered.
13. President Abraham Lincoln issued the Emancipation Proclamation.
14. The Rocky Mountains marked the western boundary of the United States.
15. The United States declared war on Mexico.
16. The United States acquired the Louisiana Territory.

II. Complete the following chart to show how the United States expanded in the 1800's.

	Date	How obtained
17. Louisiana Territory		
18. Texas		
19. Oregon Territory		
20. Mexican Cession		

Name ______________________

Class ____________

Date ____________

Independent Practice Worksheet 25.1

Nations competed for overseas empires.
(pages 569–571)

I. Identify the country described in the following statements. Some countries are described in more than one statement.

1. In 1900, it ruled one quarter of the world's land and people.

   ____

2. By the 1840's, Britain had allowed it to have a measure of self-rule.

   ____

3. By 1900, its factories were turning out one fifth of the world's total production.

   ____

4. By 1900, its empire was the second largest in the world.

   ____

5. In the late 1800's, it expanded into the Caucasus, Central Asia, and eastern Siberia.

   ____

6. In the late 1800's, its business people were financing a railroad that would stretch from Berlin to Baghdad.

   ____

7. In the late nineteenth century, its army moved into the Balkans.

   ____

II. Tell why each of the following individuals encouraged imperialism.

8. David Livingstone

   ____

9. Cecil Rhodes

   ____

10. Rudyard Kipling

    ____

Name ____________________

Class ____________

Date ____________

Independent Practice Worksheet 25.2

Imperialists divided Africa.
(pages 571–576)

I. Complete the following chart.

	Ruled by	Reasons for occupation
1. Congo River valley		develop economic resources
2. Algeria		
3. Egypt		
4. Sudan		
5. Tunisia		
6. Morocco		
7. South Africa		

II. Complete the following lists.

8. List two ways that Europeans extended their rule in Africa.

   a. ____________________

   b. ____________________

9. List two ways that European powers gained economically from their African colonies.

   a. ____________________

   b. ____________________

10. List three groups of people who competed for South Africa.

   a. ____________________

   b. ____________________

   c. ____________________

Name ____________________

Class ____________

Date ____________

Independent Practice Worksheet 25.3

The British dominated South Asia.
(pages 577–580)

List one cause and one effect for each of the following events.

1. Dozens of small Indian states, each headed by a maharajah, broke away from Mughal control.

   Cause: ________________________________

   Effect: ________________________________

2. Indian soldiers mutinied against Britain in 1857.

   Cause: ________________________________

   Effect: ________________________________

3. The British government took direct command of India.

   Cause: ________________________________

   Effect: ________________________________

4. The British promised to respect treaties made by the East India Company.

   Cause: ________________________________

   Effect: ________________________________

5. A sense of nationalism emerged among the Indian people.

   Cause: ________________________________

   Effect: ________________________________

6. Great Britain tightened its control over South and Southeast Asia.

   Cause: ________________________________

   Effect: ________________________________

Name ____________________
Class ____________
Date ____________

Independent Practice Worksheet 25.4

Imperialism threatened China.
(pages 580–583)

I. Complete the following chart by tracing the concessions that China was forced to make in the 1800's.

Country receiving concessions	Date	Territory or rights acquired
1. Great Britain	1842	a. b. c. d.
2. Great Britain	1857–1860	
3. France	1857–1860	
4. Russia	1860	
5. Japan		Ryukyu Islands
6. Japan	1890's	a. b.
7. Russia	1896	
8. France	1896	
9. Great Britain	1898	
10. Germany		Kiaochow

II. The United States responded to the events outlined above with the Open Door Policy. List four effects of that policy.

11. ____________________

12. ____________________

13. ____________________

14. ____________________

Name ______________________
Class ____________
Date ____________

Independent Practice Worksheet 25.5

Japan built a modern nation.
(pages 584–586)

Identify statements that are true of Japan by placing an *X* in front of that statement. Any statement left unmarked applies only to China.

_____ 1. Its population in 1800 was 300 million.

_____ 2. The Tokugawa shoguns ruled over a stable society.

_____ 3. The only port open to foreigners was Canton.

_____ 4. A few Dutch traders were allowed to do business in Nagasaki.

_____ 5. Matthew Perry asked the nation to trade with foreign countries.

_____ 6. It lost territory and rights in the Opium War.

_____ 7. It gave extraterritorial rights to many nations in the 1800's.

_____ 8. It signed unequal treaties with Western nations.

_____ 9. The Meiji period was a revolutionary time.

_____ 10. Its population was 430 million in 1850.

_____ 11. The rebellion by Hung Hsiu-ch'uan made many think that the country must modernize.

_____ 12. It adopted a constitution much like Germany's.

_____ 13. Some officials and the emperor believed that Western ideas and institutions were undesirable.

_____ 14. The national slogan was "Open the country to drive out the barbarians."

_____ 15. Russia took some of its territory.

_____ 16. It sent missions abroad to study foreign ways.

_____ 17. The Society of Righteous and Harmonious Fists rebelled against the "foreign devils."

_____ 18. It took Korea as a colony in 1895.

_____ 19. Its defeat of Russia in 1905 signaled its growing power as a nation.

_____ 20. It established a sphere of influence in Manchuria.

Name ______________________

Class ____________

Date ____________

Independent Practice Worksheet 25.6

Imperialism reached the Western Hemisphere.
(pages 586–589)

Identify facts in support of each of the following main ideas.

1. *Main idea:* Latin America had many resources that industrial countries needed.
   Supporting Facts:

   a. ______________________________

   b. ______________________________

2. *Main idea:* Latin America needed capital to respond to the growing demand for its raw materials and crops.
   Supporting Facts:

   a. ______________________________

   b. ______________________________

3. *Main idea:* In the 1890's, the United States interpreted the Monroe Doctrine in new ways.
   Supporting Facts:

   a. ______________________________

   b. ______________________________

4. *Main idea:* The United States had economic and strategic interests in Cuba.
   Supporting Facts:

   a. ______________________________

   b. ______________________________

5. *Main idea:* Although the Treaty of Paris gave Cuba its independence in 1899, it was under United States control for many years.
   Supporting Facts:

   a. ______________________________

   b. ______________________________

6. *Main idea:* In the late 1800's, rivalry for the Pacific islands increased among the imperialistic powers.
   Supporting Facts:

   a. ______________________________

   b. ______________________________

Name ______________________
Class ______________
Date ______________

Independent Practice Worksheet 26.1

Inventions changed ways of life.
(pages 594–597)

I. Complete the following chart.

Invention	Inventor(s)	Purpose of invention	Impact
1. Bessemer process		reduce cost of making steel	expanded use of steel
2. Industrial dynamo			
3. Electric light bulb			
4. Telephone			
5. Radio			
6. Internal combustion engine			

II. Which of the inventions listed above has had the greatest impact on modern life? Write a paragraph that identifies your choice and provides evidence in support of that choice.

Name ______________________

Class ____________

Date ___________

Independent Practice Worksheet 26.2

Science presented new ideas.
(pages 597–600)

With what new idea or discovery is each of the following individuals associated?

1. Edward Jenner

   Discovery or idea: ______________________

2. Joseph Lister

   Discovery or idea: ______________________

3. Louis Pasteur

   Discovery or idea: ______________________

4. Charles Darwin

   Discovery or idea: ______________________

5. Gregor Mendel

   Discovery or idea: ______________________

6. Robert Koch

   Discovery or idea: ______________________

7. John Dalton

   Discovery or idea: ______________________

8. Dmitri Mendeleev

   Discovery or idea: ______________________

9. Marie and Pierre Curie

   Discovery or idea: ______________________

10. Ernest Rutherford

    Discovery or idea: ______________________

Name ____________________
Class ____________
Date ____________

Independent Practice Worksheet 26.3

Women sought rights and freedoms.
(pages 601–604)

Match each statement with the correct time period or periods by placing one or more letters in the space provided.

A	B	C	D	E	F
1830–1845	1845–1860	1860–1875	1875–1890	1890–1905	1905–1920

_________ 1. Women won the right to vote in New Zealand.

_________ 2. Women won the right to vote in Australia.

_________ 3. Women won the right to vote in Finland.

_________ 4. Women won the right to vote in Norway.

_________ 5. Emmeline Pankhurst organized the Women's Social and Political Union.

_________ 6. The International Council for Women was founded.

_________ 7. No woman in Europe was allowed to vote.

_________ 8. Marie Curie became an instructor at the Sorbonne.

_________ 9. Women began to form their own unions.

_________ 10. Fifteen percent of all British unions were willing to admit women.

_________ 11. Laws limiting the working hours of women and children were passed.

_________ 12. Great Britain organized free public schools.

_________ 13. France established free public schools.

_________ 14. Only two women in France were practicing law.

_________ 15. Ten percent of all medical students in the United States were women.

Name ____________________

Class ____________

Date ____________

Independent Practice Worksheet 26.4

Art and entertainment took new forms.
(pages 604–607)

I. Identify the four art forms described in the following statements by placing the correct letter in the space provided.

I. Impressionism E. Expressionism C. Cubism P. Post-Impressionism

____ 1. This style of art shows the effects of light at a given moment.

____ 2. This art form uses a combination of lines and colors with a nature motif to encourage thought.

____ 3. In this art form, an artist uses a scene to evoke feelings.

____ 4. This style of art features geometric planes and angles.

____ 5. This style of art elicits feelings of fright and anguish.

____ 6. The early work of Pablo Picasso is representative of this style of art.

____ 7. Edvard Munch and Vasily Kandinsky were noted artists of this style of art.

____ 8. Vincent Van Gogh and Paul Gauguin were noted artists of this style of art.

____ 9. Representative artists of this style were Edouard Manet, Auguste Renoir, and Claude Monet.

____ 10. Artists who painted in this style used bright colors.

II. Identify the following individuals.

11. I based my operas on German legends.

____

12. I based my music on mathematical patterns.

____

13. I led a musical movement known as ragtime.

____

14. I produced the first feature film.

____

15. I wrote a loosely structured musical impression of the sea.

____

Name ____________________

Class ____________

Date ____________

Independent Practice Worksheet 26.5

Europe faced rising tensions.
(pages 607–611)

One way to identify main ideas is by turning headings within the chapter into questions and then reading to find answers to those questions. The following questions were written by turning headings into questions. Write an answer to each.

1. For what reasons was Germany's democracy hollow?

   a. ____________________

   b. ____________________

   c. ____________________

2. What two political crises did Britain face?

   a. ____________________

   b. ____________________

3. (a) How did the Irish question divide the British government?

   Conservatives wanted ____________________

   Liberals wanted ____________________

   (b) How was the issue resolved? ____________________

4. (a) How did the issue of the House of Lords divide the British government?

   Conservatives wanted ____________________

   Liberals wanted ____________________

   (b) How was the issue resolved?

   ____

5. What social divisions marked life in the beautiful era? ____________________

   ____

6. What crises shook Europe's fragile peace?

   a. ____________________

   b. ____________________

   c. ____________________

Name ____________________

Class ____________

Date ____________

Independent Practice Worksheet 27.1

Conflicts divided Europe.
(pages 621–624)

Events in one country often have widespread effects. Identify the effects of each of the following events.

1. After 1871, Germany, at Bismarck's urging, entered into a number of alliances.

   Effect on France: ____________________

2. Kaiser William II forced Bismarck to resign.

   (a) *Effect on Russia:* ____________________

   (b) *Effect on France:* ____________________

3. In 1894, Russia made an alliance with France.

   Effect on Germany: ____________________

4. Kaiser William II challenged Britain.

   (a) *Effect on Britain:* ____________________

   (b) *Effect on France:* ____________________

   (c) *Effect on Russia:* ____________________

5. By 1907, two rival camps existed in Europe.

   Effect on European countries: ____________________

6. Nationalism was a powerful force in the Balkans.

   (a) *Effect on Ottoman empire:* ____________________

   (b) *Effect on Austria-Hungary:* ____________________

   (c) *Effect on Russia:* ____________________

Name ____________________

Class ____________

Date ____________

Independent Practice Worksheet 27.2

Europe plunged into war.
(pages 624–626)

Write an appropriate question for each of the following answers.

1. *Answer:* Rival alliances, nationalism, and the arms race contributed to tensions among the European powers.

   Question: ____________________

2. *Answer:* Germany gave Austria-Hungary a blank check.

   Question: ____________________

3. *Answer:* Serbia was to stop all anti-Austrian activity and allow Austrian officials to investigate and try those accused of the Sarajevo assassination.

   Question: ____________________

4. *Answer:* After backing down in 1908, Russia needed to reassure its Slavic allies that it was truly the protector of Slavic peoples.

   Question: ____________________

5. *Answer:* Germany violated Belgian neutrality, which Britain had guaranteed since 1839.

   Question: ____________________

6. *Answer:* Italy regarded the Triple Alliance as a defensive alliance and therefore the alliance did not apply in a situation where Germany and Austria-Hungary were aggressors.

   Question: ____________________

7. *Answer:* French generals saw no need for defensive tactics, because victory would go to the army that attacked most vigorously.

   Question: ____________________

8. *Answer:* The Germans sent thousands of men to battlefields in the east.

   Question: ____________________

Name ______________________

Class ____________

Date ____________

Independent Practice Worksheet 27.3

The war dragged on for four years.
(pages 627–634)

I. Define the following terms by placing the correct letter in the space provided.

____ 1. "no-man's-land"

____ 2. automatic machine gun

____ 3. gas mask

____ 4. tank

____ 5. dogfight

____ 6. U-boat

a. protection from mustard and chlorine gas

b. rapid-fire weapon

c. submarine

d. aerial battle

e. space between two sets of trenches

f. armored motor vehicle

II. Explain why each of the following events was important.

7. The Battle of Tannenberg

____

____

____

8. The Russian Revolution of 1917

____

____

____

9. The entry of the United States into the war on the side of the Allies

____

____

____

10. The Battle of Amiens

____

____

____

Name ______________________

Class ______________

Date ______________

Independent Practice Worksheet 27.4

Peace stood on shaky foundations.
(pages 634–637)

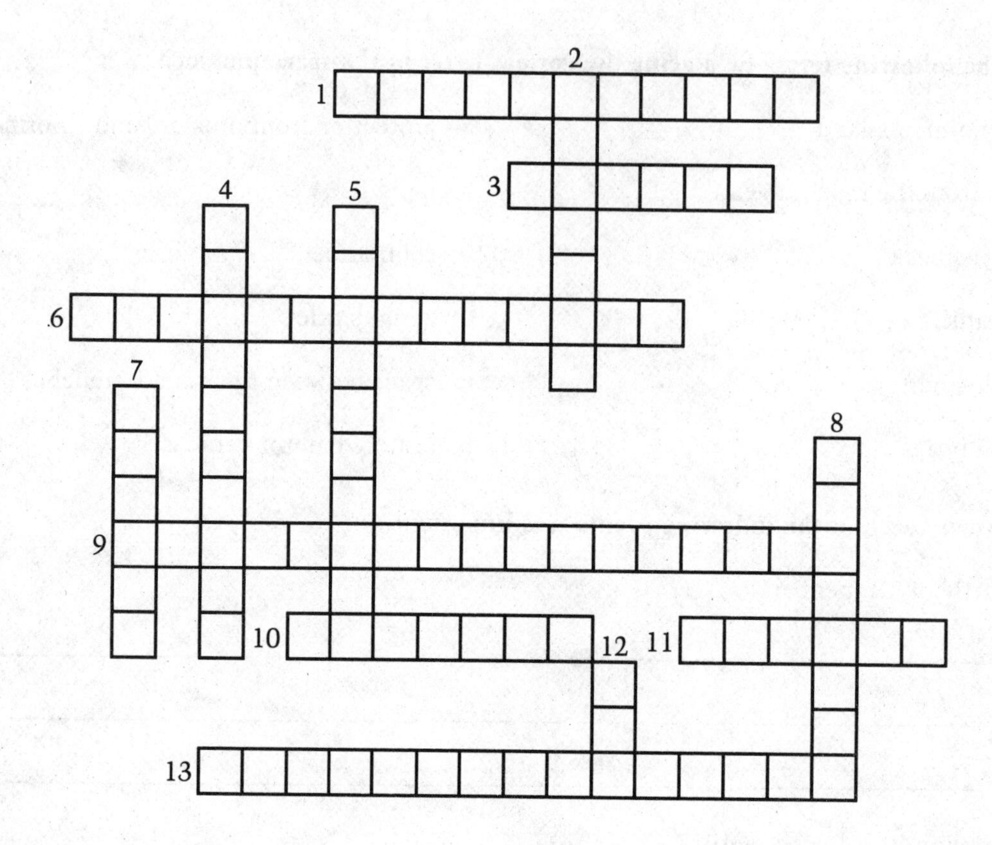

ACROSS

1. Wilson, Clemenceau, and George (3 words)
3. Regained Alsace-Lorraine
6. Wilson's peace plan (2 words)
9. Allowing people to decide for themselves under what government they wish to live
10. A nation carved from the Austro-Hungarian empire
11. Became an independent nation for the first time since the 1790's
13. An association of nations formed after World War I

DOWN

2. Lost 13 percent of its land
4. Where the peace treaty was signed
5. France's representative at the peace conference
7. The United States' representative at the peace conference
8. Territories administered on behalf of the League of Nations
12. The initials of the nation that rejected the treaty

Name ______________________

Class ____________

Date ____________

Independent Practice Worksheet 28.1

Russia struggled to reform.
(pages 641–645)

I. Identify what happened on each of the following dates, and its significance.

1. 1825

   Event: ______________________

   Significance: ______________________

2. 1853–1856

   Event: ______________________

   Significance: ______________________

3. 1861

   Event: ______________________

   Significance: ______________________

4. 1881

   Event: ______________________

   Significance: ______________________

II. The word *autocrat* means a ruler with unlimited power. Give one example of the way each of the following czars showed that he was, or was not, an autocrat.

5. Nicholas I

   Example: ______________________

6. Alexander II

   Example: ______________________

7. Alexander III

   Example: ______________________

8. Nicholas II

   Example: ______________________

Name ____________________

Class ____________

Date ____________

Independent Practice Worksheet 28.2

Russia moved toward revolution.
(pages 646–650)

I. Put the following events in chronological order, beginning with the earliest event.

____

1. Nicholas II dissolved the first Duma.
2. Lenin's brother was executed for his participation in a plot to kill Alexander III.
3. The Archduke Franz Ferdinand was assassinated.
4. Lenin returned from exile.
5. Bloody Sunday led to a series of strikes.
6. Nicholas II abdicated.
7. Nicholas II moved to the front and the czarina took charge of the government.
8. The provisional government decided to continue the war against Germany.
9. By the end of the year, there were 4 million Russian casualties.
10. A provisional or temporary government was established.
11. Rasputin died.
12. The first Duma met.
13. Lenin's policy of a "dictatorship of the proletariat" was accepted by one vote.

II. Two of the mistakes that led to the Russian Revolution and the rise of the Bolsheviks are listed below. Tell who made each error and how it affected the events that followed.

14. The decision to enter World War I

Who made the decision? ______________________________

Its significance? ______________________________

____

15. The decision to continue the war

Who made the decision? ______________________________

Its significance? ______________________________

____

Name ____________________
Class __________
Date __________

Independent Practice Worksheet 28.3

The Bolsheviks led a second revolution.
(pages 650–654)

For each of the following main ideas, provide supporting facts.

1. The events of the summer and fall of 1917 played into the hands of the Bolsheviks.

   a. ____________________

   b. ____________________

2. The Bolsheviks had three popular proposals in their platform.

   a. ____________________

   b. ____________________

   c. ____________________

3. Lenin introduced a new social order.

   a. ____________________

   b. ____________________

   c. ____________________

   d. ____________________

   e. ____________________

4. The White Army defeated itself during the civil war.

   a. ____________________

   b. ____________________

5. The civil war left Russia in ruins.

   a. ____________________

   b. ____________________

   c. ____________________

6. The New Economic Policy was a compromise with capitalism.

   a. ____________________

   b. ____________________

   c. ____________________

   d. ____________________

Name ____________________
Class __________
Date __________

Independent Practice Worksheet 28.4

Stalin became dictator.
(pages 654–657)

I. Complete the following lists.

1. List two ways that Stalin broke with Lenin's policies.

   a. ____________________

   b. ____________________

2. List four ways that Stalin's Five-Year Plan aimed to develop the Soviet Union's industry.

   a. ____________________

   b. ____________________

   c. ____________________

   d. ____________________

3. List the two main targets for Stalin's repression.

   a. ____________________

   b. ____________________

4. List three ways that Stalin's regime was totalitarian.

   a. ____________________

   b. ____________________

   c. ____________________

II. Imagine that you are a peasant in the Soviet Union during Stalin's agricultural revolution. Write a paragraph describing what is happening to you and to your family.

Name ______________________

Class ____________

Date ____________

Independent Practice Worksheet 29.1

Indians organized for independence.
(pages 661–665)

I. Rewrite the following false statements to make them true.

1. *British* tax money paid for most of the improvements in India.

2. Most of the members of the Indian National Congress were *Muslims.*

3. The *Sikhs* made up a quarter of the Indian population.

4. Mohandas Gandhi went to *Mozambique* and took a stand against its harsh racial policies.

5. In return for India's help in *the Boer War*, the British government promised reforms in India.

6. The *Government of India* Act gave the government the right to jail protestors without a trial for as long as two years.

7. The *Rowlatt* Act gave the Indian legislature shared power with the governor general.

8. In English, Gandhi's policy of satyagraha is called *"hold fast to truth."*

9. By 1924, hatred between Hindus and *Sikhs* threatened to tear apart the Indian subcontinent.

10. By 1930, the *Hindu* League was calling for separate states for Hindus and Muslims.

II. Complete the following sentences.

11. Gandhi's philosophy was based on four general principles: ______________________,
____,
____,
and ____.

12. Gandhi urged his followers to peacefully refuse to cooperate with the British by
______________, ______________, ______________,
and ______________.

Name ______________________

Class ____________

Date ____________

Independent Practice Worksheet 29.2

Nationalism spread to the Middle East.
(pages 665–669)

Identify the country described in each statement by placing the correct letter in the space provided. Some statements are true of more than one country.

A. Turkey B. Iran C. Palestine D. Saudi Arabia

____ 1. By 1918, it was all that remained of the Ottoman empire.

____ 2. In 1000 B.C., Jewish kings ruled the country.

____ 3. The laws of Islam were the laws of the country.

____ 4. All power was in the hands of the Shah.

____ 5. Women had equal political and legal rights to those of men.

____ 6. It had non-religious public schools.

____ 7. Great Britain and Russia established spheres of influence in this country.

____ 8. Ibn Saud extended his power over the country.

____ 9. In 1920, Britain took control of this country.

____ 10. It changed its name in 1935.

____ 11. It was the first republic in the Middle East.

____ 12. It was never a part of the Ottoman Empire.

____ 13. European and American companies found large deposits of oil in this country.

____ 14. By 1939, Jews made up a quarter of the population.

____ 15. The country was run like a Bedouin shaykhdom.

Name ______________________

Class ____________

Date ____________

Independent Practice Worksheet 29.3

Latin America faced difficult changes.
(pages 670–673)

Identify one effect of each of the following events.

1. Many caudillos encouraged foreigners to invest in Latin American mines and other businesses.

   Effect: ____

   ____

2. In 1910, 800 wealthy Mexican aristocrats owned 90 percent of the rural land.

   Effect: ____

   ____

3. In 1910, Mexican factory workers labored 12 to 15 hours a day for very low wages.

   Effect: ____

   ____

4. Venustiano Carranza failed to carry out the reforms of the Constitution of 1917.

   Effect: ____

   ____

5. Alvaro Obregon put into effect many of the ideas of the Constitution of 1917.

   Effect: ____

   ____

6. By 1900, the United States was the major foreign investor in Latin America.

   Effect: ____

   ____

7. Latin Americans resented United States intervention in their affairs.

   Effect: ____

   ____

8. In the 1930's, Latin American nations saw their economies collapse because of falling prices for many resources and crops.

   Effect: ____

   ____

Name ____________________
Class __________
Date __________

Independent Practice Worksheet 29.4

China overthrew its emperor.
(pages 674–677)

Identify the person described in each of the following statements by placing the correct letter in the space provided.

A. Sun Yat-sen B. Chiang Kai-shek C. Mao Tse-tung

____ 1. He distrusted the Communists.

____ 2. He assisted in the overthrow of the last emperor.

____ 3. He developed his own brand of communism.

____ 4. He almost wiped out the Chinese Communist party.

____ 5. He set out to defeat the northern warlords and unite all of China under the nationalists.

____ 6. He and his followers fled to the mountains on a journey known as the Long March.

____ 7. He based the revolution he led on the support of the peasants.

____ 8. He received money and weapons from the United States to fight Japan.

____ 9. He discovered that it was easier to destroy an old government than to build a new one.

____ 10. He promised democracy for all.

____ 11. He feared a revolution like that of the Soviet Union.

____ 12. He fought the Japanese in every way he could think of.

____ 13. He founded the Kuomintang or Nationalist People's party.

____ 14. He was more concerned with fighting the Communists than with fighting the Japanese.

____ 15. He had the support of bankers and business people.

Name ________________
Class ________
Date ________

Independent Practice Worksheet 30.1

Europe recovered from World War I.
(pages 681–683)

Complete the following lists.

1. List two effects of World War I on the nations of Europe.

   a. ____________________

   b. ____________________

2. List three reasons coalition governments tend to be unstable.

   a. ____________________

   b. ____________________

   c. ____________________

3. List four reasons the German republic was weak.

   a. ____________________

   b. ____________________

   c. ____________________

   d. ____________________

4. List three reasons the Dawes Plan helped Germany recover from the 1923 inflation.

   a. ____________________

   b. ____________________

   c. ____________________

5. List two treaties that raised hopes for peace.

   a. ____________________

   b. ____________________

Name ____________________
Class ____________
Date ____________

Independent Practice Worksheet 30.2

Society faced rapid change.
(pages 683–687)

Who am I? Identify the individual or individuals described in each of the following statements.

1. I proposed the theory of relativity.

____

2. We made the first successful flight across the Atlantic Ocean.

____

3. I wrote novels about people caught in circumstances beyond their control.

____

4. I was a novelist associated with the Harlem Renaissance.

____

5. I wrote that there are unconscious drives of which the conscious mind is unaware.

____

6. We were poets associated with the Harlem Renaissance.

____

7. I was a popular movie comedian.

____

8. I made a solo flight from New York to Paris.

____

9. I wrote poems that pictured a world drained of hope and faith.

____

10. I wrote a 1,500-page novel that focused on a single day in the lives of three Dubliners.

____

11. I was the first woman to fly across the Atlantic Ocean.

____

12. We were feminists who risked arrest for our beliefs.

____

Name ____________________

Class ____________

Date ____________

Independent Practice Worksheet 30.3

Wall Street's crash opened the Depression.
(pages 687–691)

Provide the supporting details for each of the following main ideas.

1. The stock market crash led to a serious depression.

   a. ____________________

   b. ____________________

2. The Great Depression showed clearly that there were serious weaknesses in the United States economy.

   a. ____________________

   b. ____________________

   c. ____________________

3. The effects of the Great Depression were felt worldwide.

   a. ____________________

   b. ____________________

   c. ____________________

   d. ____________________

4. Franklin D. Roosevelt started a program of relief, recovery, and reform that he called the New Deal.

   a. ____________________

   b. ____________________

   c. ____________________

5. The measures the British passed to encourage industrial growth brought slow but steady recovery.

   a. ____________________

   b. ____________________

   c. ____________________

   d. ____________________

Name ____________________

Class ____________

Date ____________

Independent Practice Worksheet 30.4

Fascist leaders became dictators.
(pages 691–698)

I. Identify the country that each statement describes by placing the correct letter in the space provided.

G. Germany I. Italy J. Japan

____ 1. Other fascist states looked to this nation as a model.

____ 2. Unemployment in this nation fell from 6 million in 1932 to 1.5 million in 1936.

____ 3. The emperor was considered divine.

____ 4. It did not permit Jews to be citizens.

____ 5. When the depression struck, military leaders took control of this country.

____ 6. Its people resented the terms of the Treaty of Versailles.

____ 7. Twenty-two state corporations ran the economy.

____ 8. It was the first to have a fascist government.

____ 9. Army leaders ruled in the emperor's name.

____ 10. The building in which its parliament met was burned.

II. Identify when each of the following events took place. Then explain why the event was important.

11. The passage of the Enabling Act

Date: ____________ Importance: ______________________________

____

12. The night of the long knives.

Date: ____________ Importance: ______________________________

____

13. The *Kristallnacht*

Date: ____________ Importance: ______________________________

____

Name ______________________
Class ____________
Date ____________

Independent Practice Worksheet 30.5

The world drifted toward war.
(pages 698–703)

I. Complete the following lists.

1. What were three reasons why the German reoccupation of the Rhineland was a turning point?

   a. ____

   b. ____

   c. ____

2. What were two reasons why Britain and France failed to take a strong stand against aggression?

   a. ____

   b. ____

3. What were two reasons why the Munich Conference marked a turning point in world history?

   a. ____

   b. ____

II. Complete the following statements.

4. The first direct challenge to the League of Nations came in 1931, when the Japanese army invaded the Chinese province of ________________.

5. Mussolini's invasion of ________________ represented a crucial test of the system of ________________ security.

6. ____________, ____________, and ____________ were called the Axis Powers.

7. The ________________ Acts banned loans and the sale of arms to nations at war.

8. When the republic collapsed in 1939, ________________ became the Fascist dictator of Spain.

9. The Treaty of Versailles prohibited an ________________, or union, between Austria and Germany.

10. The fortified region of the ________________ was the Czech's main defense against German attack.

Name ____________________

Class ____________

Date ____________

Independent Practice Worksheet 31.1

Germany overran much of Europe.
(pages 707–714)

I. For each of the following events, indicate who initiated them and in what order they occurred.

Individual	Order	Event
1. ____________	____	Invaded Albania
2. ____________	____	Agreed to divide Eastern Europe with Germany
3. ____________	____	Declared his country would never give in to the Nazis
4. ____________	____	Declared his country would serve as the arsenal of democracy
5. ____________	____	Besieged Moscow in mid-winter
6. ____________	____	Formed a government at Vichy
7. ____________	____	Invaded western Czechoslovakia
8. ____________	____	Demanded territory from Finland
9. ____________	____	Resigned as his nation decided to stand up to Hitler
10. ____________	____	Invaded Poland

II. Explain the significance of each of the following events for the course of the war.

11. Hitler's demand for the seaport of Danzig and for German railway and highway routes through the Polish Corridor

____

12. The Nonaggression Pact between Germany and the Soviet Union

____

____

13. Germany's invasion of Belgium

____

14. The terms of France's surrender at Compiègne

____

____

Name ____________________

Class __________

Date __________

Independent Practice Worksheet 31.2

Japan conquered an Asian empire.
(pages 714–718)

Providing supporting details for each of the following main ideas.

1. Japan had dreams of glory in Asia.

   a. ____________________

   b. ____________________

2. In 1941, relations between the United States and Japan were moving toward a crisis.

   a. ____________________

   b. ____________________

   c. ____________________

3. Although the Americans expected a Japanese attack, they did not know where to expect it.

   a. ____________________

   b. ____________________

   c. ____________________

4. By the middle of 1942, the flag of Japan flew over much of the Pacific.
   Japan controlled

   a. ____________________ d. ____________________

   b. ____________________ e. ____________________

   c. ____________________

5. The Battle of Midway was a turning point in the war.

   a. ____________________

   b. ____________________

Name ____________________

Class ______________

Date ______________

Independent Practice Worksheet 31.3

The Allies launched a drive to victory.
(pages 718–722)

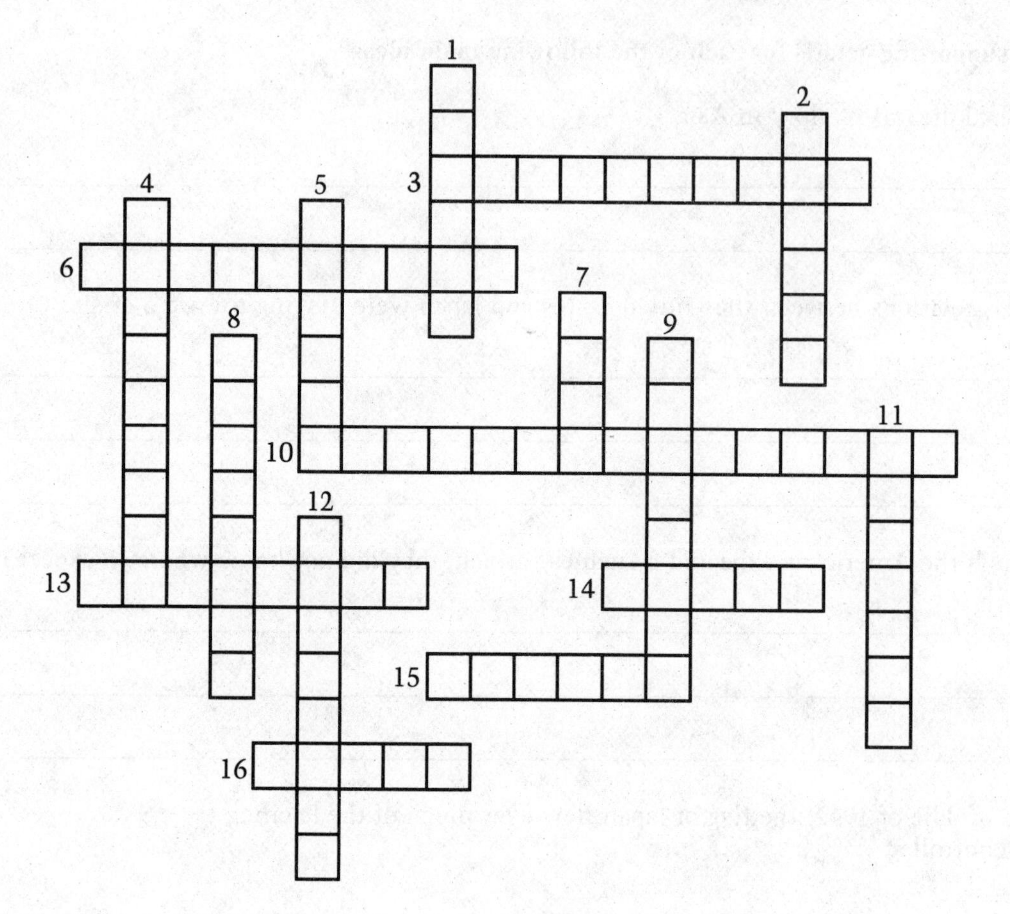

ACROSS

3. British general in North Africa
6. American general who headed the invasion of Normandy
10. An event that took place on May 7, 1945 (3 words)
13. A Japanese pilot who volunteered for a suicide mission
14. An Italian refugee who helped build the first atom bomb
15. Ordered the defense of Stalingrad at all costs.
16. Freed on August 24, 1945

DOWN

1. Known as the Desert Fox
2. Ordered use of the atom bomb
4. An atom bomb hit this city on August 6, 1945
5. The Soviet commander who defeated the Germans at Stalingrad
7. The code name for the date of the Allied invasion of France
8. Emperor of Japan
9. A Jewish refugee from Nazi Germany who helped build the first atom bomb
11. Site of a meeting between Stalin, Churchill, and Truman
12. An atom bomb hit this city on August 9, 1945

Name ____________________

Class ____________

Date ____________

Independent Practice Worksheet 31.4

World War II left a mixed legacy.
(pages 722–727)

I. List three details that support each of the following main ideas.

1. World War II caused massive destruction.

   a. ____________________

   b. ____________________

   c. ____________________

2. Hitler wanted to exterminate the Jews.

   a. ____________________

   b. ____________________

   c. ____________________

3. Many Christians resisted the Nazis' persecution of the Jews.

   a. ____________________

   b. ____________________

   c. ____________________

II. Explain the significance of the following events.

4. The production miracle ____________________

____

____

5. Women joining the work force ____________________

____

III. Explain the effect of the war on each of the following.

6. African Americans ____________________

____

7. Japanese Americans ____________________

____

Name ____________________

Class ____________

Date ____________

Independent Practice Worksheet 32.1

Two superpowers arose after World War II.
(pages 737–740)

List the supporting facts for each of the following generalizations.

1. At the end of World War II, the United States was the world's most powerful and prosperous nation.

   a. ____________________

   b. ____________________

   c. ____________________

2. The Soviet Union wanted to protect itself against future wars.

   a. ____________________

   b. ____________________

3. The United Nations was a more powerful organization than the old League of Nations.

   a. ____________________

   b. ____________________

4. The United Nations dealt more effectively with social and economic issues than political ones.

   a. ____________________

   b. ____________________

   c. ____________________

5. A new kind of arms race developed between the United States and the Soviet Union.

   a. ____________________

   b. ____________________

Name ______________________

Class ______________

Date ______________

Independent Practice Worksheet 32.2

The war left Europe divided.
(pages 740–747)

Identify the effects of each of the following events.

1. Great Britain's shift away from imperialism

   a. ____

   b. ____

2. Germany's defeat (Effects on Germany):

   a. ____

   b. ____

   c. ____

3. Soviet occupation of Bulgaria, Romania, Hungary, Poland, Czechoslovakia, and eastern Germany

   a. ____

   b. ____

4. the Truman Doctrine

   a. ____

   b. ____

5. Marshall Plan

   a. ____

   b. ____

   c. ____

   d. ____

6. the Soviet blockade of West Berlin

   a. ____

   b. ____

   c. ____

Name ____________________

Class ____________

Date ____________

Independent Practice Worksheet 32.3

Western Europe moved toward cooperation.
(pages 747–752)

Complete the following chart.

Nation	a. Key Leaders after 1945	b. Economic Trends	c. Political Trends
1. West Germany			
2. France			
3. Spain			
4. Great Britain			

Name ______________________

Class ____________

Date ____________

Independent Practice Worksheet 32.4

The USSR dominated Eastern Europe.
(pages 752–757)

I. Complete each of the following sentences.

1. Khrushchev's speech to the Twentieth Communist Party Congress signaled the beginning of a policy called ____________________.

2. Brezhnev clamped down on ____________________ who dared to protest against government policies.

3. The ____________________ claimed that the Soviet Union had the right to use force to prevent its Eastern European allies from turning away from communism.

4. When the physicist ____________________ criticized the Soviet government, he and his wife ____________________ were exiled to the remote city of Gorky.

5. In October 1956, ____________________ provoked a crisis with the Soviet Union by promising free elections and demanding that all Soviet troops leave Hungary.

6. The Hungarian revolt demonstrated that the United States policy of ____________________ did not extend to driving the Soviet Union out of its satellites.

7. On August 13, ____________, the Communists built a barrier known as the ____________________ between the two halves of Berlin.

8. East German secret police, known as the ____________________, spied upon millions of their country's own citizens.

9. ____________________ was the leader of Czechoslovakia who tried to create "socialism with a human face."

10. In August 1968, armed forces from the Soviet Union, Poland, East Germany, Hungary, and Bulgaria invaded ____________________ over four frontiers.

11. ____________________ is the name given to the brief period of reform that occurred in Czechoslovakia in 1968.

12. In 1979, the Roman Catholic Church selected a Pole, ____________________, as the new pope.

13. In August 1980, Polish workers at the shipyard in ____________________ refused to work until the government recognized their union, called ____________________.

14. In 1981, the Polish government declared ____________________, setting up military rule.

15. Solidarity leader ____________________ won the Nobel Peace Prize in 1983.

Name ____________________

Class ____________

Date ____________

Independent Practice Worksheet 33.1

Japan became an industrial giant.
(pages 761–764)

Complete the following lists.

1. List three goals of the occupation of Japan by the United States.

   a. ______________________________

   b. ______________________________

   c. ______________________________

2. List three effects of the occupation of Japan by the United States.

   a. ______________________________

   b. ______________________________

   c. ______________________________

3. List four reasons for Japan's economic miracle.

   a. ______________________________

   b. ______________________________

   c. ______________________________

   d. ______________________________

4. List four effects of Japan's economic miracle.

   a. ______________________________

   b. ______________________________

   c. ______________________________

   d. ______________________________

5. List two ways in which Tokyo might claim to be (a) the most modern city in the world, and (b) a traditional Japanese city.

   a. ______________________________

   b. ______________________________

Name ______________________

Class ____________

Date ____________

Independent Practice Worksheet 33.2

China became a Communist country.
(pages 764–767)

Complete each of the following sentences.

1. The Chinese Communist stronghold was in ______________________.
2. In their struggle to win control of China, the Communists sought the support of the ____________.
3. The Nationalist stronghold was in ______________________.
4. In 1946, the Nationalist army had an advantage in the civil war in that it ______________ and ______________________.
5. The Communist army gained strength by ______________________.
6. Even after the Communist victory, the United States continued to support Chiang Kai-shek's government on Taiwan as the legitimate government of China because of ____________.
7. From the early 1900's to 1945, Korea was occupied by the ______________________.
8. The dividing line between North and South Korea was ______________________.
9. The Soviet Union was prepared to support North Korea's attempt to take over South Korea with ______________, ______________, ______________, and ______________.
10. When North Korean troops attacked South Korea, the South Koreans were supported by troops from the ______________________.
11. Just as it appeared that North and South Korea were about to become a single country, new troops entered the conflict from ______________________.
12. In 1951, General Douglas MacArthur called for the use of nuclear weapons against ____________.
13. President Harry S Truman dismissed MacArthur because he wanted the United Nations to fight ______________________ in Korea.
14. The results of the Korean War showed that ______________ and ______________________.

Name ____________________

Class ____________

Date ____________

Independent Practice Worksheet 33.3

China changed under Communist government.
(pages 767–772)

I. Explain the changes brought about by the Communist regime in China between 1949 and 1957 in the following areas.

1. In political organization

____

2. In land reform

____

3. In industry

____

II. Identify the causes of the following events.

4. The failure of the Great Leap Forward

____

5. The split between China and the Soviet Union

____

____

III. List two consequences for each of the following events.

6. The Cultural Revolution

____

____

7. Zhou's new open-door policy

____

____

8. Deng's economic reform

____

____

9. Students' march into Tiananmen Square

____

Name ______________________

Class ____________

Date ____________

Independent Practice Worksheet 33.4

India and Pakistan became independent.
(pages 773–775)

Identify the effects of each of the following events.

1. In 1946, four days of rioting in Calcutta left more than 5,000 dead and over 15,000 injured.

____

2. On August 15, 1947, India and Pakistan became independent nations.

____

3. Nehru initiated a policy of nonalignment.

a. ____

b. ____

4. Nehru and other Indian leaders tried to modernize the country's economy.

____

____

5. Clashes between India and Pakistan took place in Kashmir and other border spots.

____

6. The Congress party won by a narrow margin in India's 1991 elections.

a. ____

b. ____

7. East Pakistanis revolted against West Pakistan's control over the nation.

a. ____

____

b. ____

____

Name ____________
Class ____________
Date ____________

Independent Practice Worksheet 33.5

The Pacific Rim faced change and conflict.
(pages 776–781)

I. Identify the colonial empires from which the following countries were formed.

1. Indonesia ____________
2. Laos ____________
3. Cambodia ____________
4. Vietnam ____________

II. Identify the country and the political regimes of the following leaders.

5. Suharto ____________
6. Ferdinand E. Marcos ____________
7. Ho Chi Minh ____________
8. Pol Pot ____________
9. Corazón Aquino ____________
10. Ngo Dinh Diem ____________

III. Complete the following sentences.

11. In its fight for independence, the ____________ used hit-and-run tactics that made the countryside unsafe for the French.
12. After their defeat at ____________, the French recognized that they had lost Indochina.
13. The ____________, as presented by John Foster Dulles, inspired the United States policy in Southeast Asia for many years.
14. The ____________ had a great deal of popular support in South Vietnam.
15. In Cambodia, a Communist government was set up by the ____________.
16. Countries of the ____________ developed into major centers of international trade.

    Four of them were named the ____________.

Name ______________________
Class ____________
Date ____________

Independent Practice Worksheet 34.1

The age of imperialism ended in Africa.
(pages 785–788)

List supporting facts for each of the following generalizations.

1. Nationalism led to a desire for independence in African colonies after World War II.

   a. ______________________

   b. ______________________

   c. ______________________

2. New nations in Africa lacked unity.

   a. ______________________

   b. ______________________

   c. ______________________

3. The legacy of colonial rule hindered economic development.

   a. ______________________

   b. ______________________

   c. ______________________

   d. ______________________

   e. ______________________

4. Colonial rule had undermined traditional ways.

   a. ______________________

   b. ______________________

5. Lack of education caused problems in new African nations.

   a. ______________________

   b. ______________________

6. The progress made by new nations depended largely upon their leaders.

   a. ______________________

   b. ______________________

   c. ______________________

   d. ______________________

Name ______________________

Class ____________

Date ____________

Independent Practice Worksheet 34.2

Africa faced social and economic challenges. (pages 789–791)

I. Explain how the following factors are connected in African nations of today.

1. Population explosion and improved health care ______________________

2. Migration to the cities and shantytowns ______________________

3. Education and leadership ______________________

4. The role of women and prosperity ______________________

II. Give examples of the following topics in various African nations.

5. Obstacles to industrial development
   a. ______________________
   b. ______________________
   c. ______________________

6. Sources of capital used for economic development
   a. ______________________
   b. ______________________
   c. ______________________

7. Obstacles to agricultural development
   a. ______________________
   b. ______________________
   c. ______________________

8. The use of English and French languages by Africans
   a. ______________________
   b. ______________________
   c. ______________________

Name ____________________

Class ____________

Date ____________

Independent Practice Worksheet 34.3

Southern Africa confronted change.
(pages 791–795)

I. Provide facts that support the following generalizations.

1. South Africa was richer in resources than any other sub-Saharan country.

   a. ____________________

   b. ____________________

2. The black South African majority had few rights and freedoms.

   a. ____________________

   b. ____________________

   c. ____________________

3. The homelands policy was unfair.

   a. ____________________

   b. ____________________

   c. ____________________

4. De Klerk transformed South African society.

   a. ____________________

   b. ____________________

   c. ____________________

   d. ____________________

II. Change each of the following statements to make it true.

5. The African National Congress (ANC) was founded in 1931, when South Africa became independent. ____________________

   ____

6. The Communists supported the rebels in Angola. ____________________

   ____

7. In South Africa, the movement toward majority rule and repeal of apartheid that F.W. deKlerk began was completed with the 1994 election of Robert Mugabe as president. ____________________

   ____

Name ____________________
Class ____________
Date ____________

Independent Practice Worksheet 34.4

New nations arose in the Middle East.
(pages 795–798)

Identify one cause and one effect for each of the following events.

1. Kurdistan was divided among Turkey, Iran, and the Soviet Union.

   Cause ____________________

   Effect ____________________

2. There was no tradition of democracy in the Middle East.

   Cause ____________________

   Effect ____________________

3. Britain turned over the responsibility for Palestine to the United Nations.

   Cause ____________________

   Effect ____________________

4. Israel declared its independence.

   Cause ____________________

   Effect ____________________

5. After the fighting in 1949, the Jews controlled half of the area defined by the UN as Arab Palestine.

   Cause ____________________

   Effect ____________________

6. Nasser seized the Suez Canal.

   Cause ____________________

   Effect ____________________

7. The Suez Canal was restored to Egyptian control.

   Cause ____________________

   Effect ____________________

8. In 1967, the Israelis made a lightning attack on Egypt, Jordan, and Syria.

   Cause ____________________

   Effect ____________________

Name ______________________

Class ____________

Date ____________

Independent Practice Worksheet 34.5

Cultural conflicts caused Middle East tensions.
(pages 799–803)

I. Give two examples of tensions caused in the Middle East by each of the following factors.

1. Religious factors

   a. ______________________________

   b. ______________________________

2. Economic factors

   a. ______________________________

   b. ______________________________

II. Identify the following individuals and list two actions taken by each of them.

3. Shah Muhammad Reza Pahlavi ______________________________

____

4. Ayatollah Ruhollah Khomeini ______________________________

____

5. Saddam Hussein ______________________________

____

6. Anwar Sadat ______________________________

____

7. Menachem Begin ______________________________

____

8. Yasir Arafat ______________________________

____

III. Explain the effects of the following conflicts.

9. The Iran-Iraq war ______________________________

____

10. The intifada ______________________________

____

Name ______________________

Class ____________

Date ____________

Independent Practice Worksheet 35.1

Key trends influenced Latin America.
(pages 807–809)

I. Complete the following sentences.

1. The ______________________ is both a political and a cultural boundary that separates the United States from Latin America.

2. When ______________________ governments failed to solve problems, they were replaced by military leaders supported by ______________________.

3. Although independent for more than a century, many Latin American countries remained ____________ dependent on industrialized countries.

4. Latin American society was composed of different ethnic groups such as the ____________, ____________, ____________, and ____________.

5. Creoles made up the ____________ in Latin American societies, while other ethnic groups were ____________ of the social pyramid.

II. Answer the following questions.

6. How did Latin American countries seek to improve economic conditions after World War II?

____

____

7. What organizations were concerned with the lower classes in Latin America? ____________

____

8. Why did slums and shantytowns develop around many Latin American cities? ____________

____

9. In what ways was Latin America involved with the international drug trafficking? ____________

____

10. What factors have increased interdependence between the United States and Latin America?

____

____

Name ______________________________
Class ____________
Date ___________

Independent Practice Worksheet 35.2

Nations sought greater stability.
(pages 810–813)

I. Match the following countries with the phrases that describe them.

A. Argentina B. Falkland Islands C. Brazil D. Chile E. Mexico

____ 1. Portuguese-speaking country

____ 2. Rich in copper

____ 3. British-owned, seized by Argentina

____ 4. Second largest country in South America

____ 5. A majority of the population are Native Americans and mestizos.

II. Match the following people with the phrases that describe them.

F. Juan Perón G. Raul Alfonsin H. Fernando Collor de Mello I. Salvador Allende J. General Augusto Pinochet

____ 6. Marxist president of Chile

____ 7. Young colonel, hero of the working class, who became president of Argentina

____ 8. Conservative president of Chile

____ 9. President of Brazil who launched economic reforms

____ 10. Elected president of Argentina in 1983

III. Identify the main cause of each of the following.

11. A group of officers drove Perón into exile.

____

12. The military government of Argentina was replaced by a democratic, civilian government.

____

13. By the early 1980's, the Brazilian economy was in chaos.

____

14. Under Pinochet, inflation in Chile dropped to less than 10 percent.

____

15. Mexico enjoyed greater political stability than most Latin American countries.

____

Name ______________________

Class ____________

Date ____________

Independent Practice Worksheet 35.3

The Caribbean Basin faced political turmoil.
(pages 813–820)

I. For each of the following countries, identify the event connected with each date listed and explain its importance in relation to democracy there.

1. Cuba ______________________

   1934 ______________________

   1959 ______________________

2. Haiti

   1957 ______________________

   1990 ______________________

   1994 ______________________

3. Nicaragua

   1933 ______________________

   1979 ______________________

   1990 ______________________

II. Complete the following sentences.

4. Two revolutionary leaders in Caribbean Basin countries, ______________________ and ______________________, became dictators.

5. The United States helped ______________ and ______________ gain their independence.

6. Among Cubans, the inclusion of ______________________ in their constitution caused much resentment toward the United States.

7. In 1952, the United States made ______________________ a self-governing commonwealth.

III. Explain the connection between the following.

8. Cuban exiles and the Bay of Pigs ______________________

   ____

9. Khrushchev and the Cuban Missile Crisis ______________________

   ____

10. The Sandinistas and Cuba ______________________

Name ____________________

Class ____________

Date ____________

Independent Practice Worksheet 35.4

The United States and Canada changed.
(pages 820–823)

I. Complete the following outline.

A. The United States

1. The United States enjoyed prosperity.

a. It emerged from World War II as the richest nation in the world.

b. ____________________

c. ____________________

2. ____________________

a. ____________________

b. The women's rights movement worked for women's rights.

c. ____________________

3. The United States role changed.

a. The nation recognized the limitations of military intervention.

b. ____________________

II. Complete the following sentences.

1. In 1988, Canada and the United States signed a Free Trade Agreement eliminating most ____________ ____________.

2. Many *Quebecois* supported separatism because they felt that they were ____________ ____________.

3. In 1980, in a ____________, or popular vote, voters in Quebec chose to remain a part of Canada.

4. Canada's new leader, Jean Chrétien, vowed in 1993 to reach a compromise with Quebec and to revive Canada's ____________.

III. Give examples of the following concepts:

5. Civil rights ____________________

6. Equal rights ____________________

7. Separatism ____________________

Name ____________________
Class __________
Date __________

Independent Practice Worksheet 36.1

The postwar era changed science and technology. (pages 831–835)

I. Explain the importance of the following to space exploration.

1. *Sputnik I* ____________________
2. John Glenn ____________________
3. Neil Armstrong ____________________
4. Space shuttles ____________________
5. Comstar ____________________
6. *Voyager 2* ____________________

II. Explain the importance of each of the following inventions to communications.

7. Fax machine ____________________
8. Transistor ____________________
9. Modem ____________________
10. Fiber-optic cables ____________________

III. Give examples of the progress made in the following areas.

11. Computers ____________________

12. Medicine ____________________

Name ____________________

Class __________

Date __________

Independent Practice Worksheet 36.2

Technology spurred global development.
(pages 835–839)

Complete the chart by indicating causes and effects of the events listed.

	Causes	Events	Effects
1.		development of multinational corporations	
2.		air pollution	
3.		water pollution	
4.		soil pollution	
5.		greenhouse effect	
6.		holes in the ozone layer	

Name ______________________

Class ____________

Date ____________

Independent Practice Worksheet 36.3

Technology had a human impact.
(pages 839–841)

I. Explain the impact of each numbered topic on the items that follow it.

1. The Declaration of Human Rights on

   a. the role of women ______________________________

   ____

   b. democracy ______________________________

   ____

   c. Amnesty International ______________________________

   ____

2. Technology on

   a. entertainment ______________________________

   ____

   b. mass culture ______________________________

   ____

   c. values ______________________________

   ____

   d. human contacts ______________________________

   ____

II. Write a short paragraph to support the statement that the world is becoming a global village.

Name ______________________

Class ____________

Date ____________

Independent Practice Worksheet 37.1

Gorbachev launched a new era.

(pages 845–852)

I. Give three examples supporting the following generalizations.

1. Gorbachev undertook an ambitious program of reform.

   a. ____________________

   b. ____________________

   c. ____________________

2. In 1989, Communist regimes in Eastern Europe collapsed.

   a. ____________________

   b. ____________________

   c. ____________________

3. The August Coup had important consequences for the Soviet Union.

   a. ____________________

   b. ____________________

   c. ____________________

II. Who am I? Identify each speaker by placing the correct letter in the blank.

___ 4. Nicolae Ceauşescu	A. A former playwright, I was elected president of Czechoslovakia.
___ 5. Mikhail Gorbachev	B. In 1990, the people of Poland elected me president.
___ 6. Vaclav Havel	C. In a failed attempt to save my country, East Germany, I opened the Berlin Wall.
___ 7. General Jaruzelski	D. My books, once banned, became legal under glasnost.
___ 8. Egon Krenz	E. I was Russia's first freely elected president.
___ 9. Alexander Solzhenitsyn	F. I was the last leader of the Soviet Union.
___ 10. Lech Walesa	G. I was the Romanian dictator overthrown and executed in 1989.
___ 11. Boris Yeltsin	H. I legalized Solidarity.

Name ______________________

Class ______________

Date ______________

Independent Practice Worksheet 37.2

The post–Cold War era brought new issues.
(pages 853–858)

Complete the lists that follow.

1. List three reasons why President Bush decided to confront Iraq's invasion of Kuwait.

   a. ____

   b. ____

   c. ____

2. List two major issues Germany faced after reunification.

   a. ____

   b. ____

3. List two ways in which shock therapy affected Poland's economy.

   a. ____

   b. ____

4. List three reasons why Yugoslavia disintegrated.

   a. ____

   b. ____

   c. ____

5. List two ways in which the war in Bosnia affected Bosnian civilians.

   a. ____

   b. ____

6. List three problems that Yeltsin faced.

   a. ____

   b. ____

   c. ____

Name ______________________
Class ______________
Date ______________

Independent Practice Worksheet 37.3

Conflicting trends shaped our world.
(pages 859–863)

I. Complete the following sentences.

1. The Internet, a global ______________ network, promises to increase communication among people all around the world.
2. A new form of mail is ______________, which allows computers to send messages to one another.
3. Improved communication technology has helped the spread of ______________, as many nations have recently turned to freely elected governments.
4. While agreements such as NAFTA lower tariffs within a certain ______________, the GATT agreements seek lower tariffs for the entire ______________.
5. When famine struck the African nation of ______________, the United States sent 25,000 ______________ to help restore order.

II. Give two examples of each of the following trends.

6. Communication revolution
   a. ______________________________
   b. ______________________________
7. Spread of democracy
   a. ______________________________
   b. ______________________________
8. Economic integration
   a. ______________________________
   b. ______________________________
9. Ethnic and religious tensions
   a. ______________________________
   b. ______________________________

Name ____________________

Class ____________

Date ____________

Independent Practice Worksheet 37.4

Human history has common themes.
(pages 864–867)

Identify the historical theme described in each event by placing the correct letter in the space provided.

A. Science and Technology B. Politics C. Economics D. Culture E. Society

____ 1. Democracy was invented by the ancient Greeks.

____ 2. Soviet leaders thought that communism would triumph around the world.

____ 3. Food and shelter are essential needs for all people.

____ 4. Democracy fought against totalitarianism in World War II and the Cold War.

____ 5. The wheel made possible countless advances in human life.

____ 6. Each group of people has its own set of moral values.

____ 7. Millions of tourists visit the Parthenon each year.

____ 8. The Ten Commandments have influenced lives for thousands of years.

____ 9. New advances in electricity helped power the second phase of the Industrial Revolution.

____10. The first nation-states began appearing in western Europe between 1300 and 1500.

____11. Different nations have different ways of distributing the goods that are produced.

____12. Under mercantilism, nations sought raw materials from their colonies.

____13. The computer may affect life as much as the wheel did.

____14. The size and composition of families vary from nation to nation.

____15. Dozens of new nations were created following World War II.

Independent Practice Worksheets Answer Key

Independent Practice Worksheet 1.1

1. (a) tools (b) bones (c) artwork
2. (a) As a result of a change in global climate, grasslands began to replace tropical rain forests in Africa. Walking erect enabled early hominids to travel more efficiently across the open grasslands. (b) Walking erect enabled early hominids to see over the grasslands in order to spot threatening animals. (c) Walking erect freed the australopithecines' hands so that they could carry food, tools, and babies.
3. (a) the Laetoli footprints (b) the remains of *Homo habilis*
4. (a) had a brain 50 percent larger than that of the australopithecines (b) made stone tools (c) lived in Africa
5. (a) Paleolithic Age (b) Mesolithic Age (c) Neolithic Age
6. (a) learned to use fire (b) first hominid to leave Africa

Independent Practice Worksheet 1.2

1. (a) There is evidence that Neanderthals buried their dead. (b) There is evidence that Neanderthals protected and cared for handicapped individuals
2. (a) Cro-Magnons lived longer than Neanderthals. (b) Cro-Magnons had advanced linguistic skills.
3. (a) Cro-Magnon devised more efficient ways of making stone blades. (b) Cro-Magnons fashioned more than 100 different tools.
4. (a) Sewing needles enabled early modern humans to make close-fitting clothing. (b) The warm pants, parkas, and boots protected early modern humans from cold Ice Age winters.
5. (a) They refused to believe that the Neanderthal bones were prehistoric. (b) They refused to believe that prehistoric artists painted the cave paintings.
6. Cro-Magnons
7. Neander Valley
8. multi-regional
9. *Homo sapiens sapiens*
10. France and Spain

Independent Practice Worksheet 1.3

1. Jarmo
2. wheat and barley
3. agriculture, towns
4. Fertile Crescent, agriculture, hunting, gathering
5. 18,000
6. arid, wheat, barley, rye
7. 10
8. 250, 25
9. bottle gourd
10. horses
11. oxen
12. rice
13. corn, beans, squash
14. Çatal Hüyük
15. obsidian, mirrors, jewelry, knives

Independent Practice Worksheet 2.1

1. Cities were centers of trade for a large region.
2. When people had a surplus of food, it was no longer necessary for everyone to farm. Then specialized jobs allowed for the development of a greater variety of goods and services.
3. provided an easy way to keep records; allowed for expression of thought
4. Many inventions that aided farming, transportation, and metalworking were developed.
5. Institutions provided the organization necessary to keep order among a large group of people and allowed the city to become even larger.
6. Israel, Jordan, Syria, Lebanon, Iraq
7. inadequate water supply, few natural resources, lack of natural defenses
8. dug irrigation ditches; traded for stone, wood, and metal; built city walls

Independent Practice Worksheet 2.2

1. Hammurabi's Code
2. divorce, own slaves, transact business, bequeath property
3. snails for dye, cedar trees
4. 600, 22
5. harder, more available, cheaper

6-C; 7-E; 8-A; 9-B; 10-D; 11-B; 12-A; 13-C; 14-C; 15-A; 16-A; 17-C; 18-B; 19-C; 20-B

Independent Practice Worksheet 2.3

1. Soldiers had iron swords and iron-pointed spears. They were trained to march and fight in tightly organized columns and divisions. Between 850 and 650 B.C., they conquered Syria, Palestine, Babylonia, and Egypt.
2. The walls of Nebuchadnezzar's palace were covered with beautiful tiles arranged in interesting patterns. The most impressive part of the palace was the hanging gardens,

which the Greeks considered one of the Seven Wonders of the World. The walls of the city were so thick that a four-horse chariot could wheel around on top of them. The highest building in the city was the ziggurat, which was 300 feet high.

3. Cyrus showed tolerance for the religions of the people he conquered. Darius divided the empire into 20 provinces in which national groups lived by their own laws within a single empire. The kings all used roads and standard coinage to hold their empire together.
4. polytheistic
5. Chaldeans
6. Indus, Nile, Black
7. Persians, Persian, Asia Minor
8. Nebuchadnezzar's

Independent Practice Worksheet 3.1

1. Upper, Lower
2. June
3. Nile River
4. agricultural districts called nomes
5. Memphis
6. Northbound boats could drift with the current.
7. The Nile left behind a deposit of fertile black soil.
8. Farmers could plant their crops on the rich soil.
9. Thousands of people starved.
10. Most Egyptians lived near the Nile. *or* The deserts protected Egyptians from invasion.

Independent Practice Worksheet 3.2

1. Pharaohs were considered god-kings. They stood at the center of Egyptian religion. The pharaoh bore full responsibility for the kingdom's well-being.
2. Peasants willingly worked for the glory of their god-king. They needed to keep busy and well-fed during the flood season.
3. A canal was built from the Nile to the Red Sea for trade. Irrigation ditches trapped and channelled water to new lands. Swamplands were drained to increase farm acreage.
4. The Egyptians learned to use bronze, horse-drawn chariots, and a new type of bow. They learned new techniques for spinning and weaving.
5. He invaded Palestine and Syria to the east. His armies also pushed as far south as the Fourth Cataract.
6. The rulers of the New Kingdom built the cliff tombs of the Valley of the Kings. They also built palaces and temples such as the giant temple of Karnak.

Independent Practice Worksheet 3.3

1. governor, general, tax collector, government official, priest
2. own property, trade property, propose marriage, seek divorce, serve as priest, serve in the government
3. army, royal treasury, priesthood, pharaoh's court
4. planting; cultivating; harvesting; building tombs, dikes, canals
5. giving baths, combing hair, cooking meals, watching children, feeding cattle
6. Egyptians believed that only the priests had magical charms and spells to protect the living and the dead from troubles of all kinds. The priests controlled more land, slaves, and wealth than the pharaoh.
7. writing or hieroglyphics; arithmetic; geometry and surveying; astronomy (the calendar); medicine

Independent Practice Worksheet 4.1

1. India's climate is dominated by seasonal winds called monsoons.
2. The Indus River changed course. *or* People overgrazed and overfarmed the land.
3. The Aryans began conquering much of northern India beginning about 1500 B.C.
4. When the Aryans arrived, their culture and that of the Indus valley dwellers blended.
5. Hindus believed that the people in high castes had done no bad deeds in former lives.

Independent Practice Worksheet 4.2

1-A, B; 2-A; 3-C; 4-B; 5-A; 6-A, B; 7-C; 8-C; 9-A, B; 10-B; 11-B; 12-A, B; 13-B; 14-C; 15-B

16. life was an endless sorrow and the way to escape was through seeking wisdom
17. nirvana
18. did not require complex rituals, was taught in the everyday language of the people
19. individual cravings and desires
20. Ashoka

Independent Practice Worksheet 4.3

1. The family was central to the society of China. A person's role in the family was fixed from birth to death.
2. The Chinese believed that royal authority came from heaven. China was ruled by a

succession of dynasties.

3. The river spread loess (yellow soil) during its floods. The river was unpredictable. It was bordered by some of the richest farmland in China.
4. Confucius was a traditionalist. He was more interested in human society than in the gods.
5. Lao Tzu believed that only the natural order of things had importance. He believed a universal force guides all things.
6. Legalists believed that a highly efficient and powerful government was the key to restoring order. They stressed punishment more than rewards. They believed in controlling ideas as well as actions.

Independent Practice Worksheet 4.4

1-B; 2-D; 3-A; 4-D; 5-B; 6-B; 7-D; 8-B; 9-D; 10-B

11. outside rival armies, resistance to his rule from within
12. commanding all noble families to live in the capital city
13. glory, unity, peace
14. the Five Classics, other writings of the past
15. Great Silk Road, the Indian Ocean

Independent Practice Worksheet 5.1

1. Seas united the Greek people. Sea travel and trade were vital to the Greek economy.
2. Three fourths of Greece is covered by mountains. Mountains made it difficult to unite the country. Tiny, fertile valleys make up about one fourth of Greece. Each was a world unto itself.
3. (a) Crete (b) mainland Greece (c) mainland Greece
4. (a) 2000–1400 B.C. (b) 1600–1200 B.C. (c) 1150–750 B.C.
5. (a) mainland Greece, Aegean islands (b) the Mediterranean region (c) little trade
6. (a) possible volcanic eruption with earthquake and tidal wave or by invasion (b) "Peoples of the Sea"
7. (a) built great palaces (b) Trojan War (c) Homer, Olympic games

Independent Practice Worksheet 5.2

1. The development of iron weapons decreased the cost of armor and swords.
2. Tyrants needed to increase their popularity and impress their neighbors.
3. The Messenian revolt was barely put down by the Spartans.
4. Solon imposed several political and economic reforms on Athens.
5. Solon and Cleisthenes enacted a series of reforms.
6. Persian armies invaded Greek territory.
7. The smaller Greek ships were able to outmaneuver the Persian ships.
8. Athens alone had challenged Persian power from the beginning.

Independent Practice Worksheet 5.3

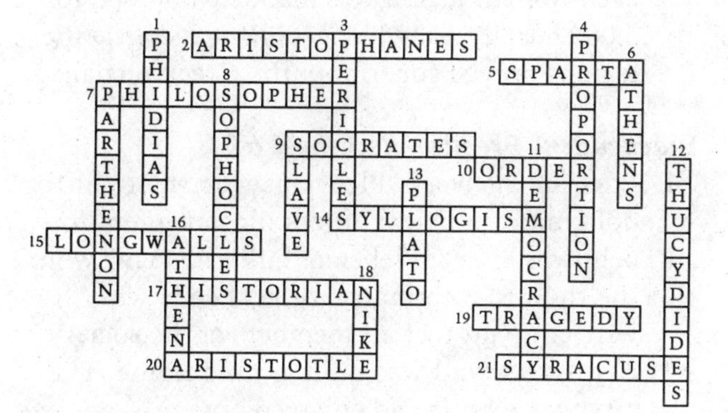

Independent Practice Worksheet 5.4

1. Eratosthenes
2. Pausanias
3. Darius
4. Demosthenes
5. Olympias
6. Isocrates
7. Philip II
8. Archimedes
9. Euclid
10. Alexander the Great
11. Hellenism
12. phalanxes
13. Companions
14. museum, library
15. Winged Victory of Samothrace

Independent Practice Worksheet 6.1

1. (a) mainland Greece (b) perhaps Asia Minor
2. (a) 750–600 B.C. (b) 1200–800 B.C.
3. (a) practice of naming gods, legends (b) taking auspices, ways of interpreting will of the gods
4. (a) contacts with Greek city-states, trade (b) writing system, architecture, trade

5. A republic was not a democracy because not all citizens had political rights; various groups struggled for power, sometimes violently.
6. Power in the family resided in the father; Roman women were in charge of the day-to-day work of running a household.
7. A small group of families dominated Rome's political life; the plebeians were free citizens but had much less power than the patricians; birth determined social and political status; the line between patricians and plebeians was very rigid.
8. The constant threat of war forced both patrician and plebeian men to serve as soldiers; each Roman legion was made up of 4,000 to 6,000 heavily armed foot soldiers; in battle the legions proved superior to the Greek phalanx.

Independent Practice Worksheet 6.2

1. *Possible answers:* Plebeians won the right to hold many political offices. Enslavement for debt was ended. Plebeians and patricians won the right to intermarry. A legal code was written to protect all members of the society.
2. A stronger wall was built around Rome. The city was rebuilt and enlarged.
3. Although he won every battle, Rome won the war.
4. Rome was able to copy the design of the Carthaginian ship. Rome proceeded to build a great fleet of similar ships.
5. Rome's victory marked the end of Carthage as a sea power. Rome took over Sicily
6. In 202 B.C., Scipio attacked Carthage.
7. Hannibal left Italy and returned to Carthage.
8. The city was destroyed and its people massacred or enslaved.

Independent Practice Worksheet 6.3

1. sell their farms
2. Rome
3. plebeians
4. Spain, Sicily, Gaul, Asia Minor, Macedon, Africa
5. Roman citizenship extended to many people in the provinces, expansion of the Roman Senate to 900 men, ordered landowners to use free men instead of slaves, set up public works programs, founded colonies to provide land for landless poor, set up a new calendar

6-E; 7-G; 8-D; 9-F; 10-H; 11-A; 12-B; 13-C; 14-I

Independent Practice Worksheet 7.1

1. the expansion of the empire's borders; the introduction of the denarius; the elimination of trade taxes; the construction of new highways; the remodeling of Rome; the establishment of the civil service
2. common coinage; elimination of taxes, road construction
3. grain supply; road repairs; postal system
4. Some emperors were corrupt, cruel, or incompetent; Rome had no clear rule of succession.
5. the rapid spread of disease in the empire; the defeat of Roman legions by Germanic tribes along the Danube

Independent Practice Worksheet 7.2

1-C; 2-F; 3-D; 4-H; 5-E; 6-F; 7-B; 8-A; 9-G; 10-C

11. art, architecture, literature, philosophy
12. Greco-Roman
13. gods, rule
14. dome

Independent Practice Worksheet 7.3

1. A.D. 45–58
2. A.D. 6
3. A.D. 66
4. 165 B.C.
5. A.D. 200
6. 65 B.C.
7. 142 B.C.
8. about A.D. 30
9. A.D. 130
10. A.D. 64
11. 4; 7; 6; 2; 8; 1; 10; 3; 9; 5
12. 129 years

Independent Practice Worksheet 7.4

1. Barbarian raids discouraged merchants from trading. Pirates terrorized Mediterranean shipping. For its many imports, Rome had to deplete its own gold and silver reserve. The silver content of coins decreased. There was a sharp decline in agricultural production.
2. The Goths defeated the Roman legions on the Danube frontier. The Persians threatened to conquer Syria and Asia Minor. Barbarians were recruited for service in the Roman army. The loyalty of the army was at times questionable.
3. The citizen population was indifferent to political matters. The army seemed to be the

only group that was interested in politics. The government found it difficult to recruit tax collectors.

4-F; 5-A; 6-D; 7-E; 8-G; 9-C; 10-B

Independent Practice Worksheet 8.1

4. 5, 3, 1, 2
6. Jerusalem
7. Byzantium
8. Aegean, Marmara
9. Greece, Asia Minor, Palestine, Syria, Egypt
10. reconquest of Roman lands to the west, compilation and simplification of the laws, rebuilding of Constantinople
11. justice, property, marriage, divorce
12. membership in the Christian Church, ability to speak Greek
13. sea walls, a moat, land walls
14. street riots, religious quarrels, palace intrigues, foreign dangers
15. Palestine, Syria, Egypt

Independent Practice Worksheet 8.2

1. the birth of Muhammad
2. First preaching by Muhammad
3. the flight of Muhammad to Medina; year 1 of the Muslim calendar
4. Muhammad's triumphant return to Mecca
5. Muslims win control of an empire stretching from the Iberian peninsula in the west to India in the east.
6. faith, prayer, alms, fasting, pilgrimage
7. the Iberian peninsula, North Africa, Egypt, Palestine, Mesopotamia, the Persian empire, northwestern India, Arabia
8. Shi'ite, Sunni

Independent Practice Worksheet 8.3

1. conflict over icons, the 1054 split in the Roman Catholic Church
2. Slav attack from the north, the 1071 attack of the Seljuk Turks on the empire, the invasion of the Ottoman Turks
3. (a) Spain; (b) Morocco; (c) Tunisia; (d) Persia; (e) Egypt
4. the attack of the Seljuk Turks, the capture of Baghdad by the Seljuk Turks
5. Kiev
6. Roman Catholic, Eastern Orthodox
7. Ottomans
8. Constantinople, Ottomans

Independent Practice Worksheet 9.1

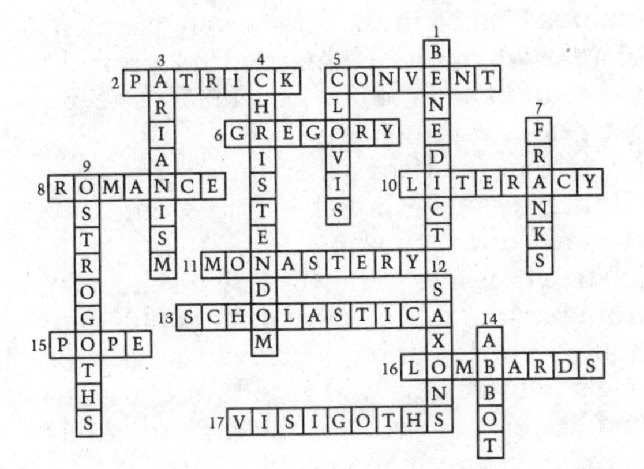

Independent Practice Worksheet 9.2

1. France
2. among their sons on the death of the king
3. major domo, or mayor of the palace
4. royal household, royal estates
5. name
6. legitimacy, Lombards
7. stirrup
8. two thirds of Italy, all of present-day France, a portion of Spain, all of German Saxony
9. counties, counts
10. administer justice, raise armies
11. missi dominici
12. judge cases, settle disputes, reward faithful followers, keep subjects in line
13. monasteries, cathedrals
14. France, Germany, the land between the two
15. Lothair

Independent Practice Worksheet 9.3

1. Ireland, Russia
2. swords, wooden shields
3. Norsemen, Northmen
4. Norway, Sweden, Denmark
5. ships
6. Iceland, Greenland
7. Leif Ericson
8. traders, farmers, artisans
9. improvements in the European system of defense, the Viking adoption of Christianity, a warming trend that allowed farming to prosper in Scandinavia
10. farm in their own land

Independent Practice Worksheet 9.4

1. (a) nobles (b) labor from all peasants, a portion of the harvest, livestock, a gift at

Christmas and Easter, payment of a tax on grain that was ground in the lord's mill and on bread baked in the lord's oven, payment of a tax when the serf married (c) protect the right of serfs to stay on the land, keep the peace, administer justice

2. (a) priests (b) tithe (c) maintain the Church, provide Church services, enforce the laws of the church
3. (a) free peasants, serfs (b) live on the manor from birth to death (c) work for nobles, give noble a portion of one's harvest and part of one's livestock, as well as gifts at Christmas and Easter, pay taxes for the right to grind grain, bake bread, marry

Independent Practice Worksheet 10.1

1. The rich soil of Europe's river valleys could now be used for farming.
2. Oxen were gradually replaced by horses, who moved faster, allowing a farmer to plow more land in a day. More land was cleared for crops.
3. Farmers could increase their food supply because they now grew food on two thirds of their land rather than half of it.
4. The population of Europe rose by about 40 percent.
5. People left the countryside to settle in towns.
6. Jews often did work that Christians could not or would not do.
7. Many serfs fled to the towns from manors.
8. The town burghers won charters granting towns certain rights in return for payments.

Independent Practice Worksheet 10.2

1. inspired the founding of similar monasteries; acted as the headquarters for Church reform
2. the cardinals would select the pope, freeing the papacy from the control of lords and kings
3. ordered priests not to marry or, if already married, to abandon present wives and children; banned lay investiture
4. granted the Church alone the right to give the bishop his ring and staff; allowed the emperor to retain the right to give a bishop the lands that went with the office
5. spread the Church's teaching more widely; brought heretics back into the Church

Independent Practice Worksheet 10.3

1. Norman lords, the Church
2. royal courts of justice
3. answer questions about the facts of a case
4. common law
5. Paris
6. granting fiefs to loyal bishops and abbots only
7. Roman Empire of the German Nation, Holy Roman Empire
8. start of Capetian dynasty; France; stability of the new dynasty helped France avoid bloody wars of succession
9. Norman victory at the Battle of Hastings; England; gave the Normans control of England, thus changing the course of English history
10. defeat of German knights by the foot soldiers of the Lombard League; German states; showed that towns could wield military power as well as economic power

Independent Practice Worksheet 10.4

1. scholars
2. orally
3. three, five
4. three, four
5. Latin
6. science, philosophy, law, religion
7. faith, reason
8. battles, pride, loyalty, justice, love
9. earthly feudal lord, heavenly master, chosen lady
10. wartime
11. Aquinas
12. middle class
13. Spanish Muslim, Constantinople
14. pages, squires, knights
15. few

Independent Practice Worksheet 10.5

1. Pope Urban II's call for the rescue of the Holy Land; start of the Crusades
2. capture of Jerusalem by the Crusaders; Christian control of the Holy Land
3. reconquest of Jerusalem by the Muslim leader Saladin; call for a Third Crusade
4. agreement for a three-year truce between Saladin and King Richard I; Muslim control of Jerusalem but visitation rights for unarmed Christian pilgrims
5. call for the Fourth Crusade; the sack of Constantinople by the Crusaders and the widening breach between East and West
6. treaty returning Jerusalem to Christian rule; excommunication of Frederick II

Independent Practice Worksheet 11.1

1-A; 2-A; 3-B; 4-A; 5-C; 6-A; 7-B; 8-A; 9-B; 10-B; 11-B; 12-C; 13-C; 14-A; 15-C

Independent Practice Worksheets Answer Key
(Continued)

Paragraphs should note that both were slowly becoming nation-states between 1300 and 1500. Students should show some understanding of the fact that in England even as the idea of a nation-state grew, the power of the monarch became more limited. In France, the idea of a nation-state grew along with the power of kings.

Independent Practice Worksheet 11.2

1. Boniface issued the bull of 1296 in an attempt to stop the taxation.
2. Philip IV of France sought to kidnap Boniface
3. Avignon became the home of the popes.
4. The English, Germans, and Italians complained that the Church was being held captive.
5. French cardinals elected another pope.
6. Each excommunicated his rival; a split known as the Great Schism took place in the Church.
7. New ideas arose.
8. Riots occurred in London.
9. He was excommunicated.
10. The Great Schism was ended.

Independent Practice Worksheet 11.3

1. (a) a plague brought by Genoese ships and transferred by fleas from infected rats (b) killed one third of Europe's population (c) mid-1300's to the 1600's (d) Europe (e) created a labor shortage; whole villages disappeared
2. (a) uprising of peasants on manors (b) rebelled when nobles refused to pay them higher wages (c) 1380's (d) England, France, Italy, Belgium (e) showed how the ideal society of the Middle Ages was breaking down
3. (a) war between England and France (b) fought over an English king's claims to land in France (c) 1337–1453 (d) France (e) forced England out of France except for Calais
4. (a) a French woman (b) led a French army against English forts that blocked the roads to Orleans (c) 1429 (d) France (e) inspired French patriotism

Independent Practice Worksheet 11.4

1-B; 2-C; 3-A; 4-A; 5-B; 6-A; 7-C; 8-C; 9-B; 10-A; 11-C; 12-C; 13-A; 14-B; 15-C

16. A class of burghers emerged.
17. Guilds were formed and burghers obtained town charters.
18. In England, Model Parliament included knights and burghers.
19. In France, the middle class became the Third Estate.
20. In England and France, monarchs chose officials from the middle class.

Independent Practice Worksheet 11.5

1. pine forest, grassy fertile steppe
2. Caspian Sea, Black Sea, Baltic Sea, Arctic Ocean
3. Don, Dnieper, Volga
4. purchases, wars, trickery, marriages
5. czar
6. west, European
7. Slavs, trading
8. northern forests
9. Russian
10. Baltic

Independent Practice Worksheet 12.1

1. Sung; improved trade network
2. T'ang; paid tribute to China, thus allowing taxes on the Chinese people to be lowered
3. Sung; brought peace on China's northern borders for 100 years
4. Sui; united northern and southern China
5. T'ang; marked the first time a woman officially ruled China
6. T'ang; gave China a remarkably intelligent governing class known as the gentry
7. marked the end of the Sui dynasty and start of the T'ang
8. Sung; gave China a valued trade item
9. Sung; speeded up the process of printing books
10. made it possible to find directions at sea

Independent Practice Worksheet 12.2

1. Pacific Ocean, Adriatic Sea
2. Abbasid, Kievan, Sung
3. Peking (Beijing)
4. caravan routes
5. Huns, Avars, Turks, Tatars

6-B; 7-B; 8-A; 9-B; 10-B; 11-C; 12-A; 13-C; 14-C; 15-A

Independent Practice Worksheet 12.3

1. The Ming emperors appointed scholar-officials who preserved the wisdom of the past by compiling a huge encyclopedia.
2. In the early 1400's, China's naval power reached its height under Admiral Cheng Ho and then collapsed abruptly when later emperors opposed naval voyages and chose isolation.
3. Peasant revolts and an invasion by the Manchus combined to bring down the Ming dynasty.

Independent Practice Worksheets Answer Key
(Continued)

4. Although the Manchus tried to keep themselves separate from the Chinese people, life under the Ch'ing was much the same as life under the Ming.

Independent Practice Worksheet 12.4

1. clans, Yamato chiefs, the Shinto religion, emperors, nobles
2. arrival of Koreans, Buddhism, the Shinto religion, emperors, nobles, Prince Shotoku, Chinese styles, pagodas, Nara, Heian
3. Heian, poetry, kana, emperors, nobles, Lady Murasaki Shikibu, feudalism, samurai, novels, shoguns
4. shoguns, Minamoto, clans, samurai, emperors, nobles, Kyoto, Kamakura, Mongol invasion, feudalism
5. the Shinto years or the age of the clans
6. the years of Chinese influence
7. the golden age or the feudal years
8. the years of the shogunate

Independent Practice Worksheet 12.5

1. daimyo
2. Country at War
3. 1543
4. silks, guns
5. Roman Catholic
6. Oda Nobunaga, Toyotomi Hideyoshi, Tokugawa Ieyasu
7. Christianity
8. Dutch
9. science, technology, military power
10. peace, stability
11. religious outlook
12. spiritual, meditation
13. wisdom
14. meditation, spiritual enlightenment
15. Zen meditation

Independent Practice Worksheet 13.1

I. B. Samudra Gupta extended the empire to the mouth of the Ganges River.
 C. Chandra Gupta II stretched the empire across northern India.
II. A. 2. The University of Nalanda attracted students from distant kingdoms.
 B. 1. Inoculations stopped the spread of smallpox. *or* A number system based on ten was developed.
III. B. Kalidasa wrote *Shakuntala*, one of the most famous plays in world literature.
IV. A. From the 400's to 1250, the Gupta empire was under constant attack.
 B. The new rulers of northern India came from central Asia and were known as the Rajputs.
V. C. During the Rajput centuries, Buddhism almost ceased to exist as a separate faith.
VI. B. Beginning in 997 and lasting for 17 successive years, a Turkish chieftain named Mahmud sacked India's cities.
VII. A. In 1191, a Turkish sultan named Muhammad Ghuri conquered much of northern India
 B. The Delhi sultanate ruled northern India for over 300 years.

Independent Practice Worksheet 13.2

1. destroyed Delhi; built a large but short-lived empire
2. overthrew the Delhi sultanate; built a new empire known as the Mughal empire
3. added new lands to the Mughal empire; showed tolerance for Hindus; created a new religion called Din Ilahi.
4. a Persian princess who married Jahangir and took control of the empire; the most powerful woman in India's history before modern times
5. built the Taj Mahal; intolerant of Hindus
6. ordered the destruction of Hindu temples; tried to turn the empire into an Islamic state
7. tried to blend Hinduism and Islam; became leader of the Sikhs

Independent Practice Worksheet 13.3

1. Seas and straits separate the islands. Five rivers cut valleys to the seas. Hills and mountains make transportation and communication difficult.
2. Southeast Asia lies on the most direct sea route between India and China. Local kings used their fleets to protect merchants from piracy.
3. Indian traders had long plyed the seaways of Southeast Asia. Buddhist missionaries were active in Southeast Asia.
4. Muslim traders brought their religion to the area. Many Muslims settled in towns and villages along the coasts.

Independent Practice Worksheet 14.1

1. Africa is the second largest continent, exceeded in size only by Asia.
2. Despite their poor soil, the savannas have always supported the largest share of Africa's population.

3. The tsetse fly influenced African history by keeping invaders out of the rain forest and by preventing African farmers from using cattle, donkeys, and horses in areas near the rain forest.
4. Africa's shoreline limited contact with the outside world. Unlike Europe, Africa has a very smooth coastline with few deep harbors.
5. The rising power of Axum played a crucial role in the fall of Meroë.
6. Sahara
7. oasis
8. desertification
9. Kushite, Piankhi
10. Ezana, Axum
11. Swahili
12. dhows
13. Malindi, Mombasa, Zanzibar
14. Zambezi, Limpopo
15. Zimbabwe

***Independent Practice Worksheet* 14.2**

1-A; 2-C; 3-A; 4-B; 5-B; 6-C; 7-B; 8-A; 9-C; 10-B

11. a group of families descended from a common ancestor
12. of a system in which a young man inherits land or wealth from his mother's brother rather than from his father
13. a person trained in the art of communicating with spirits and making predictions
14. having many rhythms
15. a person in West African society who is trained in oral record keeping

***Independent Practice Worksheet* 14.3**

1. Mississippi River; transportation
2. Amazon River
3. land bridge
4. the Tehaucán Valley
5. corn
6. American Southwest
7. modern day southern Ohio
8. along the banks of the Mississippi River

9-C; 10-A; 11-B; 12-B; 13-A; 14-C; 15-C; 16-A; 17-B

***Independent Practice Worksheet* 14.4**

1. about 100 B.C.–700 A.D.; Peru; extensive irrigation system, pyramid-shaped temples, superbly crafted jewelry, pottery, and metal work
2. 1100–1500's; Peru; built great empire, had stone fortresses without mortar, kept records by tying knots in a string, built a network of highways, built great temples
3. 1200–300 B.C.; Mexico's Gulf Coast; pottery, jade carvings, monumental stone heads, large pyramids
4. A.D. 300–900 (height of civilization); rain forests of Guatemala and Mexico's Yucatán Peninsula; stone pyramids, cities, city-states, calendar, system of writing, the concept of zero
5. A.D. 1325–1500's; Valley of Mexico; built city of Tenochtitlán, causeways, a great empire
6. Aztec, Inca
7. Inca
8. Olmec, Maya, Aztec
9. Moche, Inca
10. Maya

***Independent Practice Worksheet* 15.1**

1. the emphasis on individual glory rather than on working for the glory of God; love of classical learning; the enjoyment of worldly pleasures
2. charm; courtesy; wit; knowledge of Greek and Latin; ability to dance, write poetry, sing, play music, physical grace and strength; skill in riding, wrestling, swordsmanship
3. knowledge of the classics; ability to write, paint, make music, and dance well; charm; ability to inspire poetry and art

4-C; 5-E; 6-B; 7-D; 8-A

***Independent Practice Worksheet* 15.2**

1. textiles, banking
2. financial
3. Medici
4. free public library
5. balls, festivals, carnivals, celebrations of all sorts

6-D; 7-E; 8-A; 9-E; 10-B; 11-C; 12-A; 13-B; 14-D; 15-C

***Independent Practice Worksheet* 15.3**

1-A; 2-B; 3-C; 4-A; 5-B; 6-B; 7-C; 8-A; 9-B; 10-C; 11-A; 12-B; 13-C; 14-A; 15-C

16. belief in individualism and wordly pleasures
17. realism
18. discovery of oil paint and of perspective through use of color

***Independent Practice Worksheet* 15.4**

1. the growing demand for spices and luxury goods; the desire to spread Christianity; the ability to use new technology

2. the caravel; the astrolabe; the compass
3. Portugal; 1488; Cape of Good Hope; helped open new route to Asia
4. Portugal; 1497; water route around Africa to India; opened new sea route to Asia
5. Spain; 1492; he thought Asia but actually the Americas; discovered two continents that were new to Europeans
6. Spain; 1513; Panama; reached what is now called the Pacific Ocean
7. Portugal; 1500; Brazil; gave Portugal a claim to part of South America
8. Spain; 1519–1522; all-water route around the world; proved that the Americas were separate continents thousands of miles from Asia

Independent Practice Worksheet 15.5

1. Verrazano
2. Cartier
3. Champlain
4. LaSalle
5. Cabot
6. Raleigh
7. Winthrop
8. Hudson
9. Joliet, Marquette
10. dissenters
11. smallpox, measles, influenza
12. epidemic
13. potato
14. two, one
15. Northwest Passage

Independent Practice Worksheet 16.1

1. Popes defended the Papal States from French and Italian armies. Popes and other high Church officials lived a life of luxury.
2. During the 1400's and 1500's, groups of Christians in Europe set up strict standards for their own lives; in the Netherlands, the Brethren of the Common Life attracted many men and women; similar groups spread to other countries; as learning spread, well-educated people expected higher standards from their priests.
3. Writers criticized the corruption of Renaissance popes. Books on religion encouraged popular piety. Ideas like those of Martin Luther spread quickly because many people could read them in a short period of time.
4. Pope Leo X issued a bull threatening Luther with excommunication unless he recanted. When Luther refused, the pope excommunicated Luther. Charles V declared Luther an outlaw and heretic at the trial at Worms. Luther continued to speak out for 25 years after his trial.
5. The Germans resented sending money to Rome. Luther's talk of Christian freedom encouraged German peasants to revolt. Luther translated the Bible into German so that ordinary citizens could read it. Luther's attacks on papal greed were popular with Germans.

Independent Practice Worksheet 16.2

1. 1527; led to England's break with the Catholic Church
2. 1534; law made the English king, not the Roman pope, the official head of England's Church.
3. 1536; set forth a systematic Protestant philosophy
4. 1541; became an example of how a Protestant city was organized
5. 1567; resulted in establishing Calvinism as Scotland's official religion
6. 1523; Sweden not only won independence but also became Lutheran

Independent Practice Worksheet 16.3

1. The Jesuits founded schools throughout Europe. They converted non-Christians to Catholicism. They prevented Protestantism from spreading into new areas.
2. The group agreed on a number of doctrines. It also paved the way for reforming the Church.
3. Catholic bishops were ordered to burn the books. Throughout Europe there were huge bonfires as thousands of books were burned.
4. Protestant rulers joined together in a defensive group called the Schmalkaldic League. The Catholic princes of Germany refused to join Charles in his war against Protestantism. In 1555, Charles ordered an Imperial Diet in Augsburg to end the fighting.
5. German princes could choose to follow either Lutheranism or Catholicism. Calvinism and others forms of Protestantism were outlawed.

Independent Practice Worksheet 16.4

1. He challenged Ptolemy's geocentric (earth-centered) theory by arguing for a heliocentric (sun-centered) theory of the universe.
2. Based on Brahe's data, Kepler proposed three laws of planetary motion that confirmed the heliocentric theory. Kepler's work used a new approach called the scientific method.

3. (a) In his study of motion, Galileo found that the swing of the pendulum took the same amount of time from the first swing to last and that a falling object accelerates at a fixed and predictable rate whatever the object's weight. (b) He built the first powerful telescope to observe the moon, planets, and stars; his observations supported the heliocentric theory. (c) He established that the same physical laws operate throughout the universe.
4. He published a medical book with illustrations that showed that human anatomy was different from animal anatomy.
5. He advanced biological science by showing that the heart acted as a pump to circulate blood through the body.
6. He invented the first microscope.
7. He used a microscope to observe bacteria. He also described red blood cells.
8. He made the first thermometer that used mercury.
9. He created another scale for the mercury thermometer.
10. He developed the first mercury barometer.

Independent Practice Worksheet 17.1

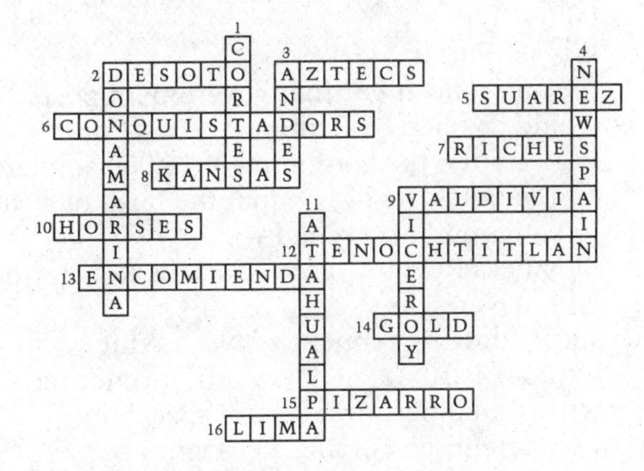

Independent Practice Worksheet 17.2

1. Philip II
2. religion
3. Escorial
4. monarchy, Roman Catholic Church
5. Christian
6. Dutch, English
7. Spanish Armada
8. pride, piety
9. debt, inflation
10. the Netherlands, France, England
11. Portugal
12. Protestantism, the Muslims
13. Dutch, sea captains, Spain
14. chivalry
15. inflation, out of

Independent Practice Worksheet 17.3

1. sister of Philip II, sent to govern the Netherlands with the twin goals of stamping out Protestantism and raising taxes; antagonized many Dutch
2. duke who led a Spanish army bent on destroying Protestantism in the Netherlands; touched off a civil war
3. greatest Dutch leader of the revolt against Spain; led the Netherlands to victory against Spain
4. a system in which people invest in business ventures in the hopes of making a profit; encouraged the growth of business and trade
5. the safest, soundest bank in Europe, acted as banker to countries throughout Europe; helped the Dutch become the bankers of Europe and enriched bank investors
6. a trading firm; helped the Dutch to establish an empire based on trade

Independent Practice Worksheet 17.4

1. Catherine, who ruled France in the name of her sons, took advantage of the division between French Catholics and Protestants to increase her own power.
2. The civil war between Catholics and Protestants resulted in the end of the Valois dynasty after a Dominican friar stabbed the king in revenge for the murder of the Catholic Duke of Guise.
3. Henry IV converted to Catholicism to end the civil war and restore peace.
4. Richelieu increased the power of the Bourbon monarchy by limiting the power of the Huguenots and the French nobility.
5. Leading French thinkers of the 1500's believed that doubting old doctrines, particularly religious ones, was the first step toward finding truth.

Independent Practice Worksheet 17.5

1. As an Austrian, he aroused the Czech's national hatred.
2. Ferdinand sent an army to put down the revolt.
3. Several German Protestant princes saw the move as a chance to challenge their Catholic emperor.
4. The Thirty Years' War began.

5. He sent French troops to join Swedish and German Protestants in the war against the Catholic Hapsburgs.
6. Trade and agriculture in Germany was in shambles.
7. Germany lost what little unity it once had. Austria and Spain declined in power. France emerged as Europe's strongest state.

Independent Practice Worksheet 18.1

1. (a) England was divided between Catholics and Protestants, both of whom wanted control of the Church of England. (b) In 1534, Henry persuaded Parliament to make him, not the pope, head of the Church of England. Thereafter, royal policy on religion changed several times as Protestants and Catholics tried to win control of the Church of England. (c) She tried to build a state church that moderate Catholics and moderate Protestants would accept.
2. (a) Mary plotted with English Catholics to unseat Elizabeth. (b) Mary wanted to become Queen of England. She had the support of Irish, Spanish, and French Catholics who wanted a Catholic queen. (c) In 1587, Elizabeth ordered Mary beheaded.
3. (a) Philip II of Spain sent an armada to invade England. (b) Elizabeth resisted Philip's plan to marry her; she encouraged Drake and the sea dogs to capture Spanish treasure; she supported Dutch Protestants in their revolt against Spain; she ordered the execution of Mary Queen of Scots. (c) The English navy, using a daring strategy, defeated the Spanish Armada, signaling the decline of Spain's political power and the weakening of Catholic forces in Europe.
4. (a) The queen was short of money for defending the country. (b) Parliament was reluctant to approve new taxes. (c) Elizabeth was stingy in paying her soldiers though generous in compliments; she encouraged the development of joint-stock companies that strengthened England economically and led to the growth of trade and colonies; she encouraged the sea dogs whose expeditions weakened Spain.

Independent Practice Worksheet 18.2

Accurate—3, 5, 6, 7, 11, 12, 13, 14, 15

16. the Spanish Armada
17. swords, cannon, cages, live animals, artificial heads
18. poet, playwright
19. Globe
20. 1576; James Burbage

Independent Practice Worksheet 18.3

1. The king and Parliament clashed constantly.
2. Parliament refused to grant Charles any money unless he signed the Petition of Right
3. The Scots gathered a huge army and threatened to invade England.
4. Charles had to call a new Parliament to raise money to defend England.
5. Charles strode into the House of Commons with 400 swordsmen and demanded the arrest of five leaders of the House of Commons.
6. The English civil war began.
7. The New Model Army refused to give up control of the country to Parliament.
8. Charles I was beheaded in 1649.

Independent Practice Worksheet 18.4

1. Prince Charles Stuart, the eldest son of Charles I
2. Restoration
3. appear before a judge who would decide whether the prisoner should be brought to trial or set free
4. religon, money
5. James II
6. Whigs, Tories
7. the announcement that government posts would be open to Catholics as well as Protestants; the stationing of 13,000 soldiers on the outskirts of London; the birth of a son to James and his second wife
8. Bloodless Revolution or Glorious Revolution
9. joint sovereigns
10. suspending Parliament's laws, taxing without Parliament's consent, interfering with a member's freedom of speech in Parliament, penalizing a citizen who petitions the king about grievances, keeping a standing army in times of peace, posting excessive bail in royal courts

11-B; 12-A; 13-A; 14-B; 15-B

Independent Practice Worksheet 19.1

1-C; 2-G; 3-B; 4-D; 5-A; 6-F; 7-E; 8-H

9. The Huguenots were critical to the success of Colbert's mercantilist policies. They were leaders in commerce, banking, and industry.
10. The Edict of Nantes protected the rights of Huguenots for nearly 100 years. When the edict was revoked, thousands fled, thereby jeopardizing France's future prosperity.

11. The palace of Versailles was built by Louis XIV and became his main residence. Its splendor was a monument to the king's greatness and taste.
12. The Treaty of Utrecht set up a new balance of power in Europe. On one side stood France and Spain. On the other side were Britain, Austria, and the Netherlands.

Independent Practice Worksheet 19.2

1. 1682	7. 1700
2. 1721	8. 1696
3. 1698	9. 1708
4. 1725	10. 1696
5. 1721	11. 1703
6. early 1600's	12. 1712

II. 6, 1, 8 and 10, 3, 7, 11, 9, 12, 2 and 5, 4

Independent Practice Worksheet 19.3

1. In Poland, the king was a foreigner dominated by the nobles. The Ottoman empire had a corrupt government and its army was poorly equipped. The Holy Roman Empire consisted of more than 300 quarreling jealous states.
2. The Hapsburgs won new territories in the War of the Spanish Succession and ruled over Austria, Hungary, and Bohemia. The Pragmatic Sanction assured a seemingly smooth transition of power from Charles VI to Maria Theresa.

3. They gained control of scattered territories. As rulers of Brandenburg, they were automatically one of the seven electors. They made strategic alliances for territory and offered the services of their army for pay.
4. The Hohenzollerns followed the example of Frederick William the Great Elector and continued to build a larger and more effective army. Frederick William I's only interest was the army, thus transforming Prussia into a military society. Army officers had a higher status than civilians.
5. The iron-rich province of Silesia was invaded and conquered. In the Treaty of Aix-la-Chapelle, Prussia officially received Silesia.
6. Austria allied with France and with Russia. Britain, the strongest naval power, allied with Prussia, the nation with the strongest army. The alliances led to the Seven Years' War.

Independent Practice Worksheet 20.1

1. formulated theory of gravity
2. fought against prejudice, superstition and intolerance; supported reason, progress, liberty
3. wrote *Encyclopedia*; made knowledge accessible and inspired the writing of other encyclopedias
4. discovered oxygen; increased understanding of the mixture of gases that make up air
5. electricity; established the connection between lightning and electric sparks
6. scientific expedition to Australia, the islands of Tahiti, New Zealand, and Hawaii; furthered knowledge of distant parts of the world
7. developed the fugue and counterpoint; considered the greatest of the baroque composers
8. wrote symphonies for strings and woodwings; considered the "father of the symphony"
9. leading classical composer; composed great operas
10. works that range from the classical to music associated with the Age of Romanticism; often called the greatest European composer of all time.

Independent Practice Worksheet 20.2

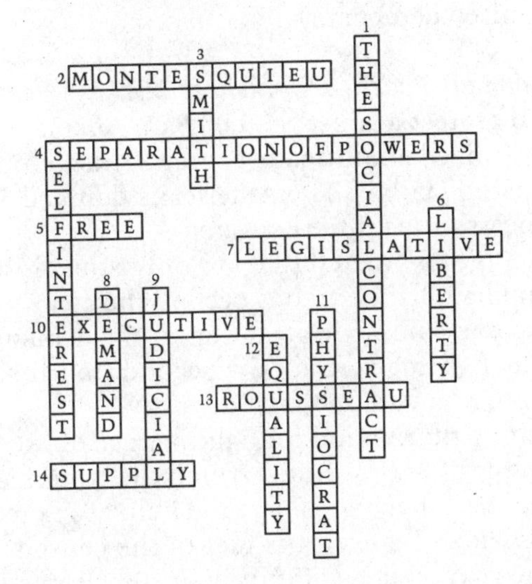

Independent Practice Worksheet 20.3

1. reduced the use of torture; allowed freedom of the press; granted religious freedom to Catholics; granted religious freedom to Protestants; admitted the evils of serfdom; called himself the "first servant of the state"
2. dedicated herself to the country's welfare; called a convention to write a contitution; wrote an essay suggesting reforms; wanted to abolish capital punishment, the use of torture, and serfdom; tried to listen to the wishes of the common people
3. discriminated against Polish and Prussian Jews; did not abolish the use of torture; did

nothing to end serfdom; waged war

4. crushed an uprising with great brutality; dropped plans for ending serfdom; gave Russian nobles absolute control over their serfs; waged war relentlessly

Independent Practice Worksheet 20.4

1. constitutional monarchy
2. cabinet
3. Sir Robert Walpole
4. king's cabinet
5. prime minister
6. five; upper classes
7. winning or controlling
8. the West Indies
9. enrich the mother country
10. help pay the costs of the Seven Years' War
11. Navigation Act
12. upper classes—town merchants and country nobles
13. Robert Walpole
14. Whigs
15. limited democracy

Independent Practice Worksheet 20.5

1. To protest against the tax, Sam Adams organized a raid against three British ships in Boston Harbor. The Americans dumped 342 chests of tea into the water.
2. George III ordered the port of Boston closed and had British troops occupy the city.
3. George paid little attention to the demands.
4. The fighting spread; The Second Continental Congress voted to raise an army.
5. strong motivation for fighting; use of hit-and-run tactics; time favored the Americans; had better generals; had the help of France
6. division of power; the idea of the consent of the governed; a commitment to reason and to a belief in human progress

Independent Practice Worksheet 21.1

1-C; 2-A; 3-B; 4-C; 5-C; 6-B; 7-C; 8-C; 9-B; 10-C; 11-C; 12-C; 13-C; 14-A; 15-C; 16-C; 17-A; 18-C; 19-A; 20-C; 21-C; 22-C; 23-A; 24-C; 25-A, B; 26-C; 27-C; 28-B; 29-C; 30-A, B

Independent Practice Worksheet 21.2

I. 7, 2, 10, 13, 3, 5, 6, 14, 15, 8, 9, 11, 12, 1, 4
16. 6, 7, 10, 13, 14
17. 1, 4, 11, 12
18. 3, 5, 15
19. 9, 1, 4
20. 2, 7, 8, 10, 14

Independent Practice Worksheet 21.3

1. Napoleon defended the palace, becoming the hero of the hour.
2. He won a series of victories that made him the most famous general in Europe.
3. Napoleon took advantage of that loss of confidence and seized power.
4. Napoleon defeated the coalition and won a peace treaty on his terms.
5. The constitution gave him all real power as First Consul.
6. slowed inflation by balancing the budget and setting up a national bank; welcomed nobles and encouraged promotions based on merit; signed an agreement with the Catholic Church and showed tolerance for Protestants and Jews; drafted a new legal code that gave the country one set of laws
7. abolished the three estates; granted equal rights before the law to all classes; established freedom of worship; promoted according to merit, not according to family

Independent Practice Worksheet 21.4

1. to destroy Britain's economy
2. Napoleon tried to make his brother Joseph king of Spain.
3. Alexander I refused to stop selling grain to Britain.
4. preferred to destroy the city rather than surrender it to the French
5. wanted to take advantage of his weakness following the Russian campaign to defeat him
6. Continental System
7. Peninsular War
8. scorched-earth
9. Elba
10. the Hundred Days; Battle of Waterloo

Independent Practice Worksheet 22.1

1. improved methods of farming increased food production; the enclosure movement forced many small farmers off the land, providing labor for industry.
2. increasing demand for food and other goods; provided extra workers for factories and other businesses
3. England and Scotland had the three resources on which industries depended—iron, coal, waterpower.
4. many fine harbors useable for trade

5. widespread interest in science and technology
6. provided loans needed to start and expand businesses

7. country at peace so business people didn't have to worry about a hostile army destroying their property; a government that encouraged economic growth

Independent Practice Worksheet 22.2

1. flying shuttle; 1733; John Kay
2. spinning jenny; 1764; James Hargreaves
3. water frame; 1769; Richard Arkwright
4. spinning mule; 1779; Samuel Crompton
5. power loom; 1785; Edmund Cartwright
6. cotton gin; 1793; Eli Whitney
7. water frame; spinning mule
8. too large and expensive for home use
9. Machines used waterpower.
10. steam engine

Independent Practice Worksheet 22.3

1. canals, macadam road, railroads
2. encouraged industrial growth; provided new jobs; boosted agriculture; changed people's perception of travel
3. United States; Belgium; Germany; Italy; France
4. produced most of the world's iron and coal; had more railroad track than any country in Europe; had an excellent merchant fleet; made foreign trade a feature of its economy

Independent Practice Worksheet 22.4

1. (a) Likely answers include better sanitation, pollution control, and building inspection.
   (b) Likely answers include group action and exerting political influence. Answers should refect an understanding that voting rights were limited in the early nineteenth century.
2. (a) Likely answers include long working hours, lack of job safety, low wages, and lack of job security.
   (b) A likely answer is forming a union. Answers should reflect an understanding that factory workers did not have voting rights in the early nineteenth century.
3. (a) Likely answers include long working hours, dangers on job, lack of adequate food.
   (b) Answers should include the fact that children under the age of 9 could no longer work. Children between the ages of 9 and 13 could work no more than 8 hours a day. Young people between the ages of 14 and 18 were limited to a 12-hour day.

Independent Practice Worksheet 23.1

1-R; 2-R; 3-C; 4-C; 5-L, R; 6-L; 7-L; 8-C; 9-R; 10-L; 11-R; 12-L; 13-C; 14-R; 15-C; 16-C, L; 17-C; 18-C; 19-R; 20-L, R

Independent Practice Worksheet 23.2

1-A; 2-B; 3-D; 4-A; 5-C, E; 6-D, E; 7-A; 8-C; 9-B; 10-D

11. George Sand
12. Emily Brontë
13. Ludwig von Beethoven
14. William Wordsworth
15. Wolfgang von Goethe

Independent Practice Worksheet 23.3

1. Toussaint L'Ouverture; 1804; France; former slaves and free men of African descent
2. Simón Bolívar, José de San Martín; 1816, 1817, 1819, 1821, 1824; Spain; creoles
3. Dom Pedro; 1822; Portugal; emperor (Dom Pedro)
4. Miguel Hidalgo, José María Morelos, Augustin de Iturbide; 1821; Spain; creoles
5. Haiti
6. Portugal
7. Spanish South America, Mexico
8. Haiti
9. Brazil
10. Mexico

Independent Practice Worksheet 23.4

1-A; 2-E; 3-D; 4-D; 5-A

II. 8, 10, 6, 7, 9, 12, 11

Independent Practice Worksheet 24.1

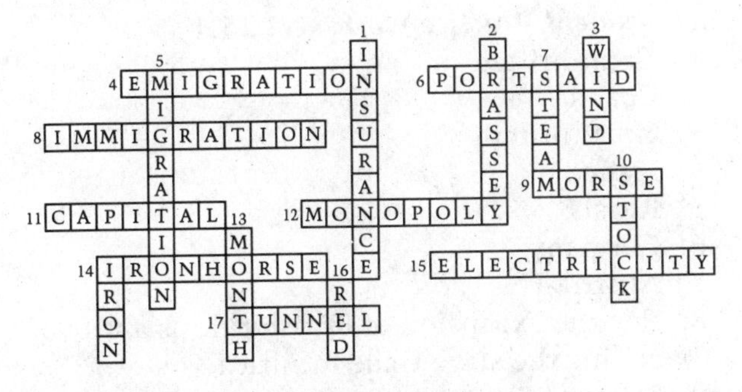

Independent Practice Worksheet 24.2

1. Owen or St. Simon or Fourier
2. Engels
3. Daumier
4. Dickens
5. James
6. Tolstoy
7. Balzac
8. the Webbs
9. Napoleon III
10. Courbet
11. Marx
12. Daumier
13. Marx
14. Owen
15. Napoleon III

Independent Practice Worksheet 24.3

1. maintained a good relationship with the other Great Powers in an effort to isolate France; offered Nice and Savoy in exchange for French support; secretly supported nationalist rebels in southern Italy; arranged meeting between Victor Emmanuel II and Garibaldi
2. undertook a war against Denmark; provoked Austria into fighting the Seven Weeks' War; provoked France into fighting the Franco-Prussian War
3. war was final step in German unification; acquired Alsace and Lorraine; ensured Prussian leadership of the new German empire
4. lost Alsace and Lorraine; had to pay Prussia five billion francs; led to the downfall of Napoleon III and the start of the Third Republic
5. In 1815, there were five great powers of about equal strength: Britain, France, Austria, Prussia, and Russia. By 1871, Prussia had become Germany, and Italy had become a sixth great power. Britain and Germany were clearly the strongest militarily and economically.

Independent Practice Worksheet 24.4

11, 7, 3, 16, 1, 14, 8, 15, 6, 10, 4, 13, 12, 2, 5, 9

17. 1803; purchased from France
18. 1845; joined the United States after winning a war of independence from Mexico
19. 1846; as a result of a treaty with Britain
20. 1848; as a result of a war with Mexico

Independent Practice Worksheet 25.1

1. Great Britain
2. Canada
3. Great Britain
4. France
5. Russia
6. Germany
7. Austria-Hungary
8. saw the expansion of British rule as a way of ending the slave trade in Africa
9. believed Britons were superior and therefore had a duty to rule much of the world
10. believed Europeans had a duty to civilize non-Europeans

Independent Practice Worksheet 25.2

1. Belgium
2. France; build prestige; stop pirates
3. Great Britain; protect Suez Canal
4. Great Britain; guard Egypt and Suez Canal, build Cairo-to-Cape Town empire
5. France; build African empire
6. France; build African empire
7. Great Britain; control diamond mines and route around the Cape of Good Hope
8. by conquest; by making alliances with certain groups in the region
9. by developing commercial plantations; by exploiting minerals
10. the British, the Boers, and the Africans

Independent Practice Worksheet 25.3

1. *Cause:* The Mughal empire was collapsing. *Effect:* The East India Company built an empire in India.
2. *Cause:* Rumors spread that British-made rifle cartridges were sealed with beef and pork fat. *Effect:* The rebellion spread to much of northern and central India. It took British troops and the East India Company over a year to put down the rebellion.
3. *Cause:* The Sepoy Rebellion took over a year of hard fighting to put down. *Effect:* India became part of the British empire.
4. *Cause:* Most of the Indian princes remained loyal during the Sepoy Rebellion. *Effect:* India was divided into two parts: the Raj, which was under direct British rule, and dozens of small states under indirect rule.

5. *Cause:* Indians resented being treated as second-class citizens in their own country. *Effect:* The Indian National Congress and the Muslim League were founded.
6. *Cause:* Britain was experiencing more competition for colonies and resources. *Effect:* Britain halted French and Russian advances into the region.

Independent Practice Worksheet 25.4

1. trade in four ports other than Canton; extraterritorial rights; repayment by the Chinese for damages to the opium trade
2. more trading rights
3. trading rights
4. Ussuri territory
5. 1879
6. Formosa, Liaotung Peninsula
7. Port Arthur, Liaotung Peninsula
8. Kwangchow
9. Weihaiwei
10. 1898

11-14 American trade rights were protected; China was protected from colonization; Europeans continued to dominate China's largest

cities; Chinese nationalism grew; the Boxer Rebellion broke out in 1900.

Independent Practice Worksheet 25.5
X—2, 4, 5, 7, 8, 9, 12, 14, 16, 18, 19, 20

Independent Practice Worksheet 25.6
1. There was a growing demand for tin from Bolivia. There was a growing demand for copper from Chile. There was a growing market for food products from Latin America.
2. Latin American governments borrowed money for improvements in transportation. Latin American landowners and business people borrowed to expand their businesses.
3. The United States acted as a negotiator in disputes between Latin American nations and European countries. The United States was willing to go to war to protect its interests in the region.
4. A number of Americans had plantations, factories, and warehouses in Cuba. The United States bought most of its sugar from Cuba. Cuba guarded the entrance to the Gulf of Mexico.
5. The United States had the right to intervene in Cuban affairs. The United States had the right to build naval bases on the island.
6. By 1900, nearly all the Pacific islands had lost their independence. The United States controlled Hawaii, Guam, and the Philippines. Britain held Australia, New Zealand, Fiji, and the southern Solomons. Germany held the northern Solomons and a number of other islands.

Independent Practice Worksheet 26.1
1. Henry Bessemer
2. Zenobe Gramme; generate electric power by using steam engines to spin electromagnets; moved electricity out of the laboratory and into everyday life
3. Thomas Edison, Humphry Davy; provide electric lighting for homes, offices, streets; gave people a way to turn night into day
4. Alexander Graham Bell; send human voice over long distances; allowed people to speak directly over long distances
5. Guglielmo Marconi; send signals through the air without wires; provided safer navigation, cheaper transmission of messages
6. Gottlieb Daimler; provide a small engine that ran on gasoline; led to the invention of the automobile and airplane

II. Paragraphs should begin with a topic sentence that identifies the writer's position. The rest of the paragraph should provide reasons and evidence in support of that position.

Independent Practice Worksheet 26.2
1. the development of a smallpox vaccine
2. the idea that infection in hospitals might be connected to filthy conditions in hospitals at that time
3. the idea that heat can destroy bacteria
4. the idea of evolution—that species change over time and new species gradually evolve
5. the idea that there is a pattern to the inheritance of traits
6. discovered the organisms that caused tuberculosis and cholera
7. the idea that matter consists of indivisible particles called atoms
8. the idea of arranging known elements by weight in a periodic table to allow the prediction of unknown elements
9. the idea that some minerals release large amounts of a powerful form of energy known as radioactivity
10. the idea that atoms contain smaller particles called electrons

Independent Practice Worksheet 26.3
1-E; 2-E; 3-F; 4-F; 5-E; 6-D; 7-A, B, C, D, E; 8-F; 9-B, C; 10-F; 11-A; 12-C; 13-C; 14-E; 15-E

Independent Practice Worksheet 26.4
1-I; 2-P; 3-E; 4-C; 5-E; 6-C; 7-E; 8-P; 9-I; 10-I

11. Richard Wagner
12. Arnold Schönberg
13. Scott Joplin
14. Edwin S. Porter
15. Claude Debussy

Independent Practice Worksheet 26.5
1. Only Reichstag elected; only the kaiser had control over the chancellor; social programs aimed at preventing revolution rather than helping workers
2. Irish question; issue of the House of Lords
3. (a) Conservatives against home rule; Liberals favored home rule (b) home rule in 1914, but by then Ireland near civil war
4. (a) Conservatives against limits on power of the House of Lords; Liberals favored limits (b) After the king threatened to add new Liberal lords, the House of Lords voted to limit its power.

Independent Practice Worksheets Answer Key
(Continued)

5. Only 1–2 percent belonged to the upper classes and 25–35 percent to the middle class; the rest lived in poverty.
6. national movements in Ireland and Norway; nationalism in Austria-Hungary, Russia, and Ottoman empire; national conflicts over the Balkan Peninsula; bitterness in France over the loss of Alsace and Lorraine

Independent Practice Worksheet 27.1

1. partial isolation
2. (a) end of treaty with Germany (b) opportunity to win Russia's friendship and end its own isolation
3. made Germany vulnerable to a war fought on its eastern and western borders
4. (a) enlarged its fleet and sought allies (b) signed treaties of friendship with Britain in 1904 and 1907 (c) signed treaty of friendship with Britain in 1907
5. Any dispute could draw the whole continent into war.
6. (a) Several Balkan groups broke away from the empire. (b) threatened the empire, which was made up of many Slavic groups also eager to have their own country; provided an opportunity to expand at the expense of the Ottoman empire (c) provided a way of gaining influence in the Balkans and winning access to the warm-water ports of the Mediterranean Sea

Independent Practice Worksheet 27.2

1. What were the causes of World War I?
2. What did Germany offer Austria-Hungary just before Austria's declaration of war?
3. What demands on Serbia did Austria-Hungary make in its ultimatum?
4. Why did Russia come to the defense of Serbia?
5. Why did Great Britain enter the conflict in 1914?
6. Why did Italy fail to support Germany and Austria-Hungary even though it had treaties with both?
7. Why did the French generals fail to use defensive tactics?
8. What weakened the German army on the Western Front in 1914?

Independent Practice Worksheet 27.3

1-E; 2-B; 3-A; 4-F; 5-D; 6-C

7. Russia lost the battle and retreated but kept pouring men into battle, thus tying up the Germans in the east.
8. led to Russian withdrawal from the war
9. tipped the balance in the Allies' favor
10. decisive battle of the war; led to ending of the war

Independent Practice Worksheet 27.4

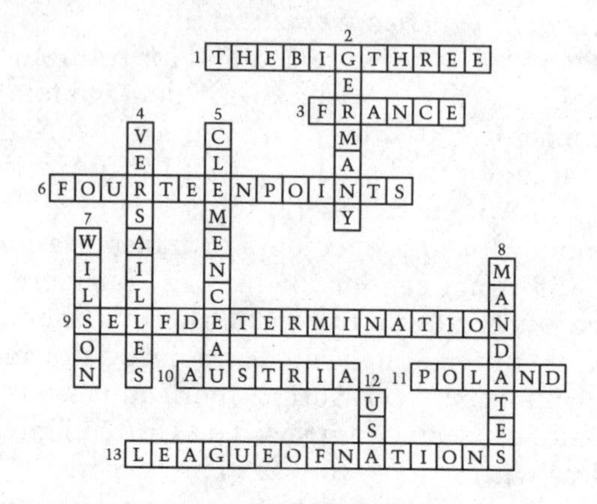

Independent Practice Worksheet 28.1

1. Decembrists revolted; encouraged Nicholas I to fight the revolutionary spirit
2. Crimean War; showed the weaknesses of the czar's government and revealed that Russian technology was far behind that of Britain and France
3. Alexander II freed the serfs; encouraged unrest as it and other reforms fell far short of what was needed
4. assassination of Alexander II; led Alexander III to reject the idea of reform and strengthen autocracy
5. Possible answers include: crushed rebellions; limited education; censored books, pamphlets, newspapers; set up secret police.
6. Possible answers include: freed serfs with a decree; gave Russians more rights; set up elected councils.
7. Possible answers include: reduced power of the zemstvos; put stricter limits on publishing; used secret police to monitor education; oppressed minority groups.
8. Possible answers include: invested national funds in local businesses; lent money to businesses; ordered tariffs to protect Russian products.

Independent Practice Worksheet 28.2

2, 13, 5, 12, 1, 3, 9, 7, 11, 6, 10, 8, 4

14. Nicholas II; showed the weaknesses of the Russian government and the nation's technology
15. Kerensky and the provisional government;

weakened the government as Russians were no more willing to fight for a provisional government than for the czar

Independent Practice Worksheet 28.3

1. The war was going badly for Russia, thus increasing discontent. General Lavr Kornilov tried to seize power. By stopping him, the Bolsheviks won much popular support.
2. to protect the revolution from czarists and generals; to end Russia's participation in the Great War; land reform as a number one priority
3. division of land among the peasants; a truce with Germany; government takeover of industries; the running of factories by workers' councils; establishment of a dictatorship of the proletariat
4. The Whites argued among themselves. They lost the support of the peasants and workers when they threatened to restore farms and factories to their original owners.
5. Factories were destroyed; trade had ceased; many workers were dead or in prison.
6. Farmers could sell their surplus. Individuals could make a profit on their sales. Private ownership was allowed for some businesses. Foreign investment was encouraged.

Independent Practice Worksheet 28.4

1. Stalin was not concerned with the revolution outside the Soviet Union; he was committed to establishing a command economy in both agriculture and industry through centralized planning.
2. It sought industrial growth throughout the country, especially in Siberia; set specific targets for each industry; limited production of consumer goods and invested in mines, heavy industry, railroads, and energy resources.
3. religion—He closed churches and forbade the teaching of religion in schools.
   the Communist party itself—He brought to trial and executed long-time Communists who had fought for the revolution or held positions in Lenin's first government.
4. Stalin was an absolute dictator; he crushed his enemies or anyone suspected of becoming an enemy; the secret police did his bidding; his decision controlled who worked, where they worked, and what they did.

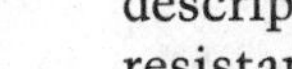

II. Answers will vary but should include a description of the peasants' hardships and resistance to Stalin's orders as well as the brutal repression by the government to enforce change.

Independent Practice Worksheet 29.1

1. Indian
2. Hindu
3. Muslims
4. South Africa
5. World War I
6. Rowlatt
7. Government of India
8. passive resistance, civil disobedience
9. Muslims
10. Muslim
11. live simply, be tolerant of the religious beliefs of others, spend life in the service of others, battle injustice in all its forms without resorting to violence
12. boycotting British goods, refusing to pay British taxes, refusing to obey British laws, refusing to attend British courts

Independent Practice Worksheet 29.2

1-A; 2-C; 3-D; 4-B; 5-A; 6-A; 7-B; 8-D; 9-C; 10-B; 11-A; 12-B; 13-B; 14-C; 15-D

Independent Practice Worksheet 29.3

1. Caudillos and outsiders got rich. The common people gained nothing.
2. Peasants lived at the mercy of the rich landowners. The anger of the peasants led to revolution.
3. In 1910, they joined with peasants in a revolution.
4. He was overthrown and Alvaro Obregón took power and put many of the ideas of the 1917 constitution into effect.
5. The civil war ended and Mexico achieved political stability.
6. The United States intervened in Latin America time and time again to protect its own economic interests.
7. The United States announced the Good Neighbor Policy in 1933 as part of its efforts to improve relations with Latin America but resentment continued.
8. Governments encouraged the growth of national industries or nationalized foreign companies within their nation.

Independent Practice Worksheet 29.4

1-B; 2-A; 3-C; 4-B; 5-B; 6-C; 7-C; 8-B; 9-A; 10-B; 11-B; 12-C; 13-A; 14-B; 15-B

Independent Practice Worksheets Answer Key
(Continued)

Independent Practice Worksheet 30.1

1. decline of European dominance in world affairs; the rise of new democracies
2. hard for one party to win enough support to govern effectively; seldom last long; hard to provide leadership toward long-term goals
3. lack of democratic traditions in Germany; country divided among many political parties; government bore the burden of defeat; Germany faced enormous economic problems, including skyrocketing inflation
4. lent $200 million from American banks to stabilize German currency; set a more realistic schedule for reparation payments; attracted further loans and investments from the United States
5. 1925 treaty between France and Germany; Kellogg-Briand peace pact

Independent Practice Worksheet 30.2

1. Albert Einstein
2. John Alcock, Arthur Brown
3. Franz Kafka
4. Claude McKay
5. Sigmund Freud
6. Countee Cullen, Langston Hughes
7. Charlie Chaplin
8. Charles Lindbergh
9. T.S. Eliot
10. James Joyce
11. Amelia Earhart
12. Margaret Sanger, Emma Goldman

Independent Practice Worksheet 30.3

1. Within a few months of the crash, unemployment rates rose. Industrial production, prices, and wages fell.
2. The supply of industrial goods exceeded the demand. A surplus of agricultural products drove prices down. People were speculating wildly in the stock market.
3. American investors began to recall loans to cope with the crisis at home. This withdrawal dealt a hard blow to the economy of western Europe. World manufacturing fell by 38 percent. International trade dropped by 65 percent. Unemployment skyrocketed.
4. He started large public works projects to provide jobs for the unemployed, and government agencies that helped businesses and farms. For the first time, the United States government spent public money on welfare and relief programs. He also tried to remove some of the problems that had caused the depression—for example, agencies were set up to regulate banking and the stock market.
5. The national government passed high protective tariffs. It increased taxes. It regulated the currency. It lowered interest rates.

Independent Practice Worksheet 30.4

1-I; 2-G; 3-J; 4-G; 5-J; 6-I, G; 7-I; 8-I; 9-J; 10-G

11. 1933; gave Hitler the right to make law without the consent of the Reichstag
12. 1934; shocked the German people into total obedience
13. 1938; signaled a significant escalation in the Nazi effort to wipe out the Jewish population

Independent Practice Worksheet 30.5

1. (a) Hitler's daring action strengthened his power and prestige within Germany. (b) The reoccupation of the Rhineland changed the balance of power in Germany's favor. (c) France's and Britain's weak responses encouraged Hitler to begin a program of military and territorial expansion.
2. (a) The Great Depression forced both nations to deal with serious economic problems at home. (b) The suffering caused by World War I created a deep desire for peace.

3. (a) Chamberlain's failure to stand up to Hitler helped to make World War II inevitable. (b) Democratic leaders vowed that they would never again appease a ruthless dictator.
4. Manchuria
5. Ethiopia; collective
6. Germany, Italy, Japan
7. Neutrality
8. Francisco Franco
9. Anschluss
10. Sudetenland

Independent Practice Worksheet 31.1

1. Mussolini; 2
2. Stalin; 3
3. Churchill; 7
4. Roosevelt; 9
5. Hitler; 10
6. Pétain; 8
7. Hitler; 1
8. Stalin; 5
9. Chamberlain; 6
10. Hitler; 4
11. Hitler's demands convinced Britain and France that appeasement was no longer possible.

12. It shocked the world because the Nazis had come to power by attacking the Communists; it assured Hitler that Germany would not face a two-front war.
13. The German army swung around the Maginot Line, surprising the French army.
14. France was divided between the north—occupied by Germany—and the south—under Vichy's government; Pétain was seen by many as a traitor, and De Gaulle would soon organize the French underground; Britain was left alone to face Germany.

Independent Practice Worksheet 31.2

1. called its planned empire Greater East Asia Coprosperity Sphere; took over Manchuria; tried to capture China's heartland
2. Roosevelt was determined to keep Japan from taking over China. Japan threatened American-controlled Philippines. The United States banned the shipment of American fuel, scrap iron, and steel to Japan.
3. The United States code-breaking revealed that the Japanese were preparing for war. United States officials predicted that the Japanese would attack the Philippines; no one foresaw that Pearl Harbor would be a target; experts believed it was too far from Japan and too well defended; the United States forces in Pearl Harbor were taken completely by surprise.
4. Manila; Bataan; Corregidor; Hong Kong; Guam and Wake; Malay Peninsula; Java, Borneo, Sumatra, and Celebes; Burma
5. Hawaii was never threatened again; Japanese advance halted; Allies now on the offensive

Independent Practice Worksheet 31.3

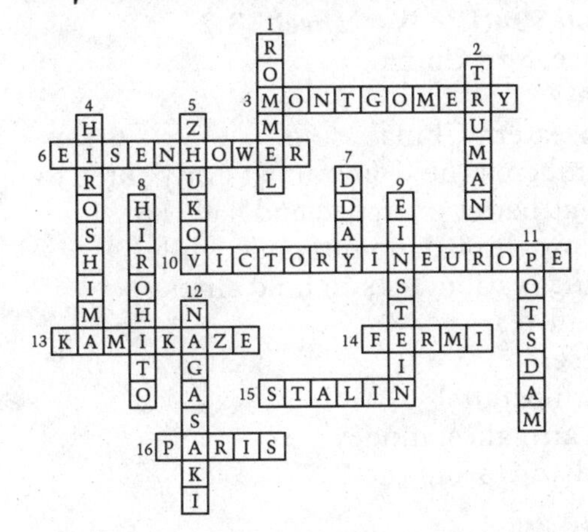

Independent Practice Worksheet 31.4

1. War dead reached at least 40 million; the cost in property damage was devastating; millions of displaced persons wandered around Germany and Japan, and thousands starved to death after the war ended.
2. As Nazi armies invaded Eastern Europe, SS units had orders to kill as many Jews as possible; Polish Jews were herded into overcrowded ghettos sealed off from the rest of the city; death camps were organized to kill the entire Jewish population; this act of genocide is known as the Holocaust.
3. Many Christian families hid Jews in their homes; the Archbishop of Toulouse defied the Nazis; a Swedish diplomat backed by the Catholic Church and the Swedish government successfully protected thousands of Jews.
4. United States industry's ability to produce warplanes, trucks, warships, and tanks changed the course and outcome of the war.
5. Women took the place of men in the work force; this experience changed the attitudes of many about women's roles.
6. Many African Americans from the rural South found higher paying jobs in defense industries in the Northeast and Midwest; African American soldiers came home determined to end racial discrimination.
7. A wave of prejudice against Japanese Americans caused thousands of Japanese to be moved to internment camps, making them lose their homes and their businesses.

Independent Practice Worksheet 32.1

1. American cities and factories were untouched by the war. The United States had the largest and best-equipped armed forces in the world. The United States had sole possession of the atom bomb.
2. Large areas of the Soviet Union had been occupied by the Nazis during the war. Stalin wanted Eastern Europe as a buffer zone for protection in the future wars.
3. All major powers joined; peacekeeping forces could enforce its decisions or separate warring groups.
4. UNESCO improved literacy. FAO sought to feed the world's hungry. WHO tried to improve health standards.
5. By 1949, the Soviets had their own atom bomb. By 1952, the United States had a hydrogen bomb.

Independent Practice Worksheet 32.2

1. After ruling over a fourth of the world's land, Britain gave up most of its colonies, withdrew from Palestine, and made fairly peaceful agreements with its former colonies.
2. transportation at standstill; most of country's businesses destroyed; country divided into four zones (later into two separate nations)
3. Communist governments in Albania, Bulgaria, Romania, Poland, Hungary, Czechoslovakia; division of Europe into democratic Western Europe and a Soviet-controlled Eastern Europe
4. Greece remained politically part of Western Europe; United States worked to contain communism in Europe.
5. stabilized currencies in countries receiving aid; increased agricultural and industrial production; exports kept American economy booming
6. Berlin airlift; Soviets back down; improved relations between Germany and its allies

Independent Practice Worksheet 32.3

1. (a) Konrad Adenauer; Willy Brandt; Helmut Kohl (b) rebuilding the economy; competitiveness of products for export and in the EC (EU) (c) joining NATO, improving relations with Societ bloc, recognizing East Germany
2. (a) Charles de Gaulle; Georges Pompidou; Valery Giscard d'Estaing; François Mitterand (b) economic boom after WWII; support of the EC (EU) (c) loss of colonies; many political parties, unstable coalition governments; withdrawal from NATO; improved relations with Soviet bloc
3. (a) Francisco Franco; Juan Carlos (b) lack of industry; low per capita income; improvement as Northern Europeans discovered Sun Belt and as a result of EC (c) shift from dictatorship to democracy
4. (a) Margaret Thatcher; John Major (b) outdated factories; loss of colonial products and markets; nationalization of industry; brief boom in 1950's; in 1980's tax cuts and return of industry to private ownership resulted in economic problems initially; North Sea oil reversed that situation. (c) alternated between Labour and Conservative parties; religious conflict in Northern Ireland; peace process begun in 1994

Independent Practice Worksheet 32.4

1. de-Stalinization
2. dissidents
3. Brezhnev Doctrine
4. Andrei Sakharov; Yelena Bonner
5. Imre Nagy
6. containment
7. 1961; Berlin Wall
8. Stasi
9. Alexander Dubcek
10. Czechoslovakia
11. Prague Spring
12. John Paul II
13. Gdansk; Solidarity
14. martial law
15. Lech Walesa

Independent Practice Worksheet 33.1

1. demilitarization; democratization; revival of the Japanese economy
2. demilitarization; democratization; land reform and modernization of industry
3. effective use of imported technology; productive labor force; high rate of savings; government encouragement of economic growth
4. urban growth; pollution; press for more openness in Japanese society; changing roles for women
5. (a) metropolitan area of more than 11 million people, electronics capital, world's busiest stock exchange (b) ancient Buddhist temples, traditional sports, Kabuki drama, tea ceremonies

Independent Practice Worksheet 33.2

1. northwestern China
2. peasants
3. southwestern China
4. outnumbered the Communist army three to one; was better equipped and had U.S. aid
5. spreading through countryside while allowing Nationalists to hold cities
6. the Cold War
7. Japanese
8. the 38th parallel
9. tanks, airplanes, money
10. United States and the UN
11. China
12. Chinese cities
13. limited war

14. Communist China was great power; neither the United States nor the Soviet Union could gain a clearcut victory in a limited war

Independent Practice Worksheet 33.3

1. The Communist party sets policy; the government implements it.
2. Mao took the land from the landlords and divided it among the peasants; he forced the peasants to join collective farms.
3. Mao nationalized all private companies, quadrupled the production of steel, and doubled the output of coal, cement, and electricity.
4. Peasants resented the vast, impersonal communes; crop failures caused a famine; poor planning hampered industrial growth.
5. The Chinese resented their role as Moscow's junior partner; angered Soviets by making some independent decisions in foreign policy; the long shared border between the two countries was a source of conflict.
6. Colleges and schools were shut down; thousands of people were executed or died in jail; factories were closed; farm production declined.
7. The United States ended its opposition to admitting the People's Republic of China to the United Nations; President Nixon made a visit to China to meet with Mao and Zhou; the leaders agreed to begin cultural exchanges and trade; the U.S. and China established formal diplomatic relations.
8. Deng eliminated the communes and leased the land to individual farmers; he permitted small private businesses to produce goods and services and gave more freedom to managers of large state-owned industries to plan production; he welcomed foreign technology and investment. Students questioned the lack of political freedoms and rights.
9. Students won widespread popular support, Deng ordered crackdown, which left hundreds dead and thousands wounded Massacre resulted in worldwide protests.

Independent Practice Worksheet 33.4

1. British leaders decided that partition was the best way to limit bloodshed.
2. Fighting broke out between Hindus and Muslims.
3. Nehru refused to take sides in the Cold War; India and other countries that chose to remain nonaligned came to be known as the Third World and became a new influence in world politics.
4. Indians began to adopt modern farming techniques. Industry grew slowly but steadily.
5. A full-scale war began in 1965.
6. BJP agitators encouraged Hindu riots; Hindus tore down a Muslim mosque; Hindu-Muslim violence spread across India.
7. Rioting broke out and developed into a full scale civil war, India entered the war and forced Pakistan to surrender; East Pakistan became the independent nation of Bangladesh.

Independent Practice Worksheet 33.5

1. Dutch
2. French
3. French
4. French
5. Indonesia, dictatorship
6. Philippines, dictatorship
7. Vietnam, Communist dictatorship
8. Cambodia, Communist dictatorship
9. Philippines, democratic rule
10. South Vietnam, dictatorship
11. Vietminh
12. Dien Bien Phu
13. domino theory
14. Viet Cong
15. Khmer Rouge
16. Pacific Rim; Four Tigers

Independent Practice Worksheet 34.1

1. An educated elite became the nationalist leaders who worked to end colonial rule; African soldiers who fought with colonial powers during World War II wanted to gain their own freedom; the example of nations in the Middle East gaining their independence offered inspiration.
2. Most of the new nations were based on the colonial units set up by Europeans; the boundaries of these units showed no regard for boundaries between ethnic and rival groups.
3. The colonies had been developed to provide resources and raw material for the colonial rulers rather than crops and materials for people of the colonies; workers were paid low wages while the profits went to foreign businesses; much of the land was still foreign owned; many of the countries were at the mercy of world markets because their

economy depended on the export of one cash crop or resource.
4. Thousands of men had been forced to work in the mines and were away from their families for months or years; forced migrations disrupted communities and weakened traditional ties and customs.
5. The new nations lacked professional people as leaders and skilled workers to aid in economic development; the low rate of literacy made it difficult to develop stable governments.
6. Most countries in Africa fell prey to one-man rule; leaders such as Houphouet-Boigny of the Cote d'Ivoire brought decades of peace to his country; in Uganda, Amin was a ruthless dictator ruling according to his own cruel whims; in Zaire, Mobutu ruled as an absolute dictator; in Kenya, Kenyatta worked to overcome old rivalries, involved leaders from other groups in government, and worked for Kenya's economic development.

Independent Practice Worksheet 34.2

1. Progress against disease reduced death rates.
2. Cities were unable to cope with the sudden increase in population due to migration.
3. As education improves, new leaders are being trained.
4. Woman play a key role in African society.
5. lack of capital and of a skilled or an educated population; income spent on food rather than economic development because of the growing population.
6. loans; export of mineral resources; to a lesser degree, export of agricultural products
7. Much of Africa's agriculture consists of subsistence farming; African soil is mostly unsuitable for intensive or machine cultivation; drought has reduced land suitable for herding or farming.
8. The use of French and English has helped communication among African people who speak many different dialects; African authors have achieved success by writing in English or French; English and French have helped to connect Africa to the rest of the world.

Independent Practice Worksheet 34.3

1. Africa's temperate climate and fertile soil gave it the choicest farmlands; it was rich in mineral resources and a leading producer of gold and diamonds.
2. Blacks could not vote or hold seats in parliament; they lacked freedom of speech, assembly, and press; they were denied equal treatment and opportunity in many spheres of life.
3. The homelands policy only set aside 13 percent of the lands for blacks, who made up 75 percent of the population; this land was the poorest in resources; thousands of black families were forced to move to the homelands, while millions of blacks had jobs in the white areas outside the homelands; this caused the splitting of families and the building of shanty towns by blacks near the cities.
4. He integrated public facilities, abolished the registration system, lifted the ban on ANC, opened the National party to blacks, freed Nelson Mandela, and worked for a transition to majority rule.
5. The ANC was founded in 1912, the first such organization on the continent and long before South African independence.
6. The South African government supported the rebels against a Communist government.
7. The movement toward majority rule and the repeal of apartheid that F.W. deKlerk began was completed with the 1994 election of Nelson Mandela as president.

Independent Practice Worksheet 34.4

1. *Cause:* National boundaries were drawn by former European rulers.
   Effect: Millions of Kurds lost their homeland.
2. *Cause:* The Middle East had been part of the Ottoman empire. *Effect:* Most countries were ruled by hereditary princes; where overthrown, these princes were replaced by military leaders.
3. *Cause:* Efforts to reach a compromise between Arabs and Jews failed. *Effect:* The UN recommended the creation of two Palestines—one for the Jews and one for the Arabs.
4. *Cause:* Jewish immigration had built up in Palestine; the UN had decided that part of Palestine should become a Jewish state.
   Effect: Six Arab states attacked Israel.
5. *Cause:* The Jews defeated the Arabs and kept conquered territory from the Arab section of Palestine. *Effect:* Egypt and Jordan occupied the rest of Palestine; Arab refugees settled in camps along the borders of their homeland.

6. *Cause:* Nasser—motivated by nationalism and anger at the United States' and Britain's refusal to finance the Aswan Dam—decided to nationalize the Canal. *Effect:* Britain and France, aided by Israel, took back the Canal by force.
7. *Cause:* The UN condemned Britain and France, and so they backed down. *Effect:* Their defeat encouraged Britain and France to let go of their African empires; Nasser became a great Arab hero.
8. *Cause:* Nasser moved to close the Gulf of Aqaba to Israel. *Effect:* total defeat of the Arabs; Israel kept Arab Jerusalem and other conquered territories.

Independence Practice Worksheet 34.5

1. the revolution in Iran: conflict between fundamentalists and those who favored a secular regime; the civil war in Lebanon between Muslims and Christians
2. tensions within oil-rich countries between modern and more traditional life-styles; tensions between oil-producing countries and western oil companies; tensions between OPEC and the western world

3. Shah of Iran; tried to westernize Iran; used secret police to punish his opponents
4. Iranian religious leader; led the opposition to the Shah; roused Iranians to rebellion; established an Islamic theocracy in Iran; encouraged Muslim fundamentalists in other Arab countries to seize power
5. Iraqi military ruler; fought a war against Iran; used chemical weapons against Iran
6. president of Egypt; arranged to meet Menachem Begin; signed treaty with Israel recognizing Israel's right to exist
7. Israeli prime minister; met with Sadat; signed a treaty with Egypt ending 30 years of hostility
8. leader of the PLO; vowed to eliminate Israel and create an independent Palestinian state; later recognized the right of Israel to exist and renounced terrorism
9. enormous casualties and destruction on both sides; end of Khomeini's dream of extending the Islamic revolution.
10. focused world attention on Palestinian demands for an independent state; increased pressure on Israel to reach an agreement with Palestinians on the future of occupied lands and on an independent Palestinian state

Independent Practice Worksheet 35.1

1. Rio Grande
2. civilian; wealthy landowners
3. economically
4. creoles, Africans, mestizo, and Native Americans
5. elite or upper class; at the bottom
6. by diversification, nationalizing of key industries, import substitution, foreign loans
7. trade unions; the Catholic Church
8. The population dramatically increased; millions migrated from rural areas to the cities; the cities were not prepared to receive this massive influx of people.
9. Latin American countries were the most important producers of drugs; in these countries, drug lords formed powerful cartels that could use bribery, threats, and violence.
10. shared problems such as drug trade, debt crisis, and preservation of the environment; growing immigration from Latin America to the United States where Hispanics have become the fastest growing ethnic group

Independent Practice Worksheet 35.2

1-C; 2-D; 3-B; 4-A; 5-E; 6-I; 7-F; 8-J; 9-H;10-G

11. Peron's policies had made him enemies among landowners, wealthy businessmen, and especially former colleagues in the military.
12. Argentina's defeat in the Falkland Islands
13. foreign debts in part from the construction of Brasília but also from the financing of the 1960's economic boom; the increase in population and the uneven distribution of wealth
14. returned copper mines to American business, allowed landowners to regain holdings, foreign investments returned
15. In Mexico, the army was less important politically than in other Latin American countries so that civilian governments were formed with participation of the Native American and mestizo majority.

Independent Practice Worksheet 35.3

1. Batista came to power and eliminated democratic freedom and representation; Castro came to power and established a Communist dictatorship
2. François Duvalier seized power and established dictatorship; Duvalier's son was overthrown and free democratic elections brought Aristide to power; Aristide, exiled by military junta in 1991, returned to assume office.

3. Samoza came to power and established a dictatorship; Samoza was overthrown by the Sandinistas, who launched economic reforms but soon switched to a dictatorship under Ortega; Ortega agreed to hold free elections, and Chamorro was elected in the first democratic transfer of power in Nicaragua.
4. Castor, Ortega
5. Cuba, Panama
6. the Platt Amendment
7. Puerto Rico
8. Cuban exiles with the help of the CIA took part in the La Brigada expedition against Cuba, intending to overthrow Castro and to set up a rebel government. Outnumbered, they were defeated and forced to surrender.
9. Khrushchev sent missiles with nuclear warheads to Cuba, Kennedy announced a blockade to prevent the arrival of the new missiles and demanded the removal of those already in Cuba. Khrushchev backed down but asked that the United States pledge not to invade Cuba.
10. The Sandinista government asked for military aid from Cuba.

Independent Practice Worksheet 35.4

I. A. 1. b. Innovation led to technological superiority.
c. United States companies became multinational corporations.
2. The postwar era brought changes.
a. The civil rights movement worked for equal rights for African Americans.
c. Opposition built up against the Vietnam War.
3. b. The nation's economy continued to grow despite deficits in the balance of payments and in the budget.

II.
1. trade barriers
2. discriminated against
3. referendum
4. economy

III.
5. the right to vote or hold office
6. equal pay for similar work and equal access to job opportunities
7. the *Quebecois* in Canada

Independent Practice Worksheet 36.1

1. the world's first artificial satellite
2. the first United States astronaut to orbit the earth
3. the first man to step on the moon
4. spacecraft that could return to earth under their own power
5. communications satellite that helps to transmit messages and pictures around the earth
6. scientific space probe launched by the United States that has reached Neptune and now left the solar system for the stars
7. machines that can transmit copies over the telephone
8. a tiny electronic device that has made possible the transistor radio, many instruments and communications systems, and the computer
9. a device that enables computers to communicate by telephone
10. cables that will replace telephone wiring and will be able to carry large amounts of data and images as well as voice
11. Progress in microtechnology such as transistors and the silicon chip have helped to make both mainframe computers and powerful personal computers. Supercomputers have been developed that use parallel processing and high definition TV. These have increased the computer's ability to perform complex tasks and produce higher quality images.
12. Advances in surgery include use of the laser, use of robotics, heart bypass operations, pacemakers, and organ transplants. New drugs such as antibiotics, vaccines, and insulin have reduced or eliminated certain diseases and their complications. Genetic research has helped scientists understand cell growth and development and has potential for treating certain inherited diseases.

Independent Practice Worksheet 36.2

1. *Causes:* Improved transportation and communication have enabled businesses to spread to several countries and to make use of cheap labor and resources in developing countries. *Effects:* They have brought prosperity to the industrialized world where the headquarters are located; they have brought employment and the development of resources to less developed countries, but the profits have often gone to owners overseas unless the developing country was strong enough to nationalize.

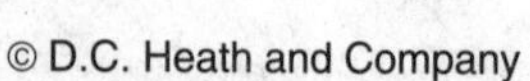

2. *Causes:* increased use of fossil fuels, chemicals used in industry *Effect:* acid rain
3. *Causes:* acid rain, accumulated wastes, oil spills, chemicals *Effects:* destruction of life in ponds, lakes, and oceans
4. *Causes:* acid rain, accumulated wastes, chemicals *Effects:* destruction of vegetation, poisoning of crops and of animals
5. *Causes:* excess carbon dioxide in the atmosphere that traps heat; the destruction of rain forests *Effects:* changing of world climate leading to desertification, shrinking polar ice caps, and a rise in the level of the oceans that will threaten low-lying lands
6. *Cause:* use of chlorofluorocarbons in refrigerating systems and aerosol sprays *Effects:* Through holes in the ozone layer, harmful ultraviolet radiation is likely to penetrate, causing cancer and destroying plant life.

Independent Practice Worksheet 36.3

1. (a) reinforces the idea that women should be treated as equals; is likely to broaden women's roles in traditional societies and reinforce the cause for equal rights in industrialized societies
   (b) upholds principle of democracy by recognizing the worth and dignity of the individual and the right to freedom and equality
   (c) keeps track of violations of human rights as defined by the declaration
2. (a) Televison has added a visual dimension to home entertainment; VCR's have led to a movie revival; communications satellites have widened TV's influence even to influencing the outcome of ongoing events; transister radios, tape players and CD's have broadened musical entertainment.
   (b) Mass culture has broadened worldwide, extending across time and space to include cultures from different continents and from the past.
   (c) It has encouraged materialism, the wish for more possessions and the urge for immediate satisfaction of needs.
   (d) It tends to isolate people and to make contacts less personal.

II. Answers will vary but should emphasize the greater closeness, interdependence, and understanding promoted by expanded communication and transportation. The sharing of information and of cultural events has encouraged mutual influence between cultures.

Independent Practice Worksheet 37.1

1. (a) Glasnost made Soviet society more open.
   (b) Perestroika brought economic reform.
   (c) Demokratizatsiya introduced limited democracy.
2. (a) Poles voted the Communists out of power.
   (b) Radical reformers voted the Hungarian Communist party out of existence.
   (c) Loss of public support forced the East German Communist party to disband.
3. (a) There was a wave of popular contempt and rage against the party.
   (b) The Soviet parliament voted to suspend all party activities.
   (c) The Soviet republics seceded from the Soviet Union, causing its collapse.

4–G; 5–F; 6–A; 7–H; 8–C; 9–D; 10–B; 11–E

Independent Practice Worksheet 37.2

1. (a) to prevent Iraq from gaining control of the world's oil supply
   (b) to stop Iraq's nuclear weapons program
   (c) to deter other potential aggressors
2. (a) rebuilding the East German economy
   (b) confronting neo-Nazi violence
3. (a) immediate, dramatic rise in unemployment and inflation
   (b) slow recovery of the economy
4. (a) ethnic and religious differences among the groups
   (b) rivalries among the provinces over access to government income
   (c) Milosevic's program of Serbian nationalism
5. (a) As many as 200,000 died in the fighting.
   (b) Two million people were forced to flee their homes.
6. (a) The economy suffered from high inflation, high unemployment, and low output.
   (b) Yeltsin's conservative political opponents challenged him.
   (c) Many people disapproved of Yeltsin's decision to use force against Chechnya.

Independent Practice Worksheet 37.3

1. computer
2. e-mail
3. democracy
4. region, world
5. Somalia, troops

6. (a) growth of Internet
   (b) increase in number of personal computers
7. (a) collapse of communism in the Soviet Union and Eastern Europe
   (b) expans6f democracy in Latin America
8. (a) entry of formerly Communist nations into world trade market
   (b) NAFTA and EU regional trade agreements
9. (a) Hindu-Muslim violence in India
   (b) civil war in Rwanda

Independent Practice Worksheet 37.4

1–B; 2–C; 3–E; 4–B; 5–A; 6–E; 7–D; 8–D; 9–A; 10–B; 11–C; 12–C; 13–A; 14–E; 15–B